Halvor

A Story of Pioneer Youth

BY Peer Strømme

TRANSLATED FROM THE NORWEGIAN AND ADAPTED

BY Inga B. Norstog and David T. Nelson

Luther College Press: DECORAH, IOWA

Printed by
The Anundsen Publishing Company
Decorah, Iowa

CONTENTS

Introduction

Halvor brings us the enchantment of another age, yet it deals with real persons, places, and events. This delightful tale rescues for present and future generations a period that once flourished but has passed away, that bloomed with youthful vigor but is forever gone. There is something fresh and unspoiled and unpretentious about the story. It has the fragrance of sincerity. In part it is autobiographical, with some characters and places clearly delineated and others only thinly disguised. In part it is a son's tribute to his father and to all the pioneer parents for whom the author had so warm an affection.

Peer Olsen Strømme, oldest of thirteen children, was born September 15, 1856, on a farm southwest of Winchester, a village twelve miles west of Neenah and Menasha, Wisconsin. He died September 15, 1921, at Madison, Wisconsin, and is buried there. His parents were Ole Olsen Strømme, who emigrated from Strømme in Vraadal, Telemark, Norway, in 1844, and Eli Haugen, who arrived in America four years later. After attending Luther College from 1869 to 1876 (he once ran away from college but was induced by a friend to return) and Concordia Seminary in St. Louis, Missouri, from 1876 to 1879, he was ordained to the Lutheran ministry. He was a pastor near Ada, Norman County, Minnesota, 1879-86; and near Nelson, Wisconsin, 1886-87. From 1881 to 1886 he was superintendent of schools in Norman County; in 1887 he taught at St. Olaf College, Northfield, Minnesota; he was later principal of Mt. Horeb Academy, Mt. Horeb, Wisconsin, 1893-94.

In 1879 he married Laura Marie Ericksen, one of eight gifted daughters of Olaus Erickson, builder and contractor of Lansing, Iowa. The Strømmes had six children.

At various times Strømme held editorial positions on eight newspapers and two magazines; he wrote three novels, a volume of poems, and one of memoirs. He translated a dozen or more books, some from Norwegian to English, some from English to Norwegian, and some from German to Norwegian.

He made five trips to Europe and two around the world. He was a war correspondent in Berlin in 1915. Few men were more popular on the lecture circuit. Among his fellow Norwegian Americans he was best known as a traveler, newspaper correspondent, lecturer, and humorist.

Halvor made its first appearance serially under the title "Hvorledes Halvor Blev Prest" in the Superior (Wisconsin) *Posten* (November 24, 1892—June 8, 1893), when Strømme was trying to breathe life into that all but defunct paper; but the narrative did not then include the chapters on St. Louis and the hero's pastorate. The story was immediately popular and brought in about a thousand new subscribers. "For many years," says Strømme, "I had nursed the idea that perhaps I could write a story truthfully portraying pioneer life. . . . But the tale was a product of haste. I had to write it in the few hours that were left over from editorial work and from translating advertisements and reading dunning letters and hiding out from my creditors. I wrote at a furious pace—a few pages at a time—whenever the paper needed something to fill a column. But that first part of the story was nevertheless so well received that I plucked up courage to complete it and publish it in book form. During the summer in Chicago and the fall in Mt. Horeb I made a great many needed corrections, wrote the conclusion, and completed arrangements with B. Anundsen of *Decorah-Posten* to publish the book."[1]

The book appeared at Decorah, Iowa, in 1893 in an edition of 3,000 copies. It was again run as a serial in *Normanden* of Grand Forks, North Dakota, (May 18—August 31, 1910) and then was re-issued in book form at Grand Forks the same year.

[1] Strømme, *Erindringer* (Memoirs), Minneapolis, 1923, 321.

In 1936 Inga Bredesen Norstog's English translation was published under the title *How Halvor Became a Minister*. Mrs. Norstog, whose husband was the well-known Norwegian-American poet Jon Norstog, was director of the Norwegian-American Historical Museum in Decorah from 1947 to 1959. In her preface Mrs. Norstog wrote: "Winchester Town . . . is the Springville so vividly pictured in this book. In fact, most of the story is the autobiography of this son of Norwegian immigrants. . . . He was himself the little Halvor who, because he was so bright, was slated to become a minister, in the pioneer mind the highest station to which a mortal could aspire, and who at great sacrifice was sent to Luther College, Decorah, Iowa, and to Concordia Seminary, St. Louis, and who through it all remained the same likable, wholesome, and altogether human fellow."

Some time ago Mrs. Norstog asked me to undertake the necessary revisions and corrections in her English version, which she had made in the midst of a crowded schedule, never seeing proofs before it appeared in print. While I was doing so, I received many suggestions from those kind enough to read the manuscript. Encouraged by them, I have been emboldened to tighten up the story by omitting two chapters—"The American Saloon" and "Trouble in the Congregation"—neither of which mentions the hero. I have cut minor irrelevant details to speed the story and, to escape the abrupt ending of the original, have largely rewritten the last few pages, beginning with the reference to the election controversy. For the sake of those who have difficulty with Norwegian pronunciations, I have renamed Halvor's godparents "Jens" and "Helga." Mrs. Norstog,

8

before she was incapacitated by the illness which led to her death, read the first draft of my revision. But the adaptations were made later and she has not seen them. In so far as the story now presented is "adapted," I therefore bear the responsibility.

Those who read Norwegian will find in Strømme's *Erindringer* many of the raw materials from which he constructed the narrative.

Fridtjof Schroder, assistant professor of art history at the University of Cincinnati, kindly drew the sketches which appear in this edition. Merald E. Wrolstad of the Cleveland Museum of Art gave valuable suggestions as a typographical consultant.

I acknowledge with gratitude my indebtedness to Clara J. Paulson, John C. Bale, and Oivind M. Hovde of the Luther College faculty; Helga Lund Algyer of Decorah; Helen T. Katz of St. Paul; my daughter, Elizabeth Nelson Seegmiller of Decorah; and my wife, Esther Torrison Nelson, who has shared most of the labor.

DAVID T. NELSON
LUTHER COLLEGE

CHAPTER ONE

Soren sets sail
for a new world

Soren Helgeson came to America in the early fifties. All he owned was what he wore on his back, as the saying goes, but in reality he was rich. He had splendid health, great physical strength, a good conscience, a happy disposition, and an altogether excellent appetite. He looked out on the world through a pair of honest gray eyes which shone with a zest for life and with unconquerable courage. He was his own master. He feared God, but no man.

Moreover, at home in Tuddal, Telemark, in southern Norway, he had a treasure which he would not have exchanged for all the riches of America. On a little cotter's place in the shelter of Gausta Mountain a certain sweet and comely girl had promised before he left Norway that she would come to him as soon as it could be managed.

"First you must find a place for a home," she had said, "then you can send me a ticket."

"Ah," thought he, "that will not take long in America. There money grows on trees and good workers get big wages." He was sure he would soon send for her; his heart warmed at the thought.

It had been hard for Soren to leave Signe. Yet, since he had barely been able to scrape together enough money to get to the promised land himself, there had been no other way. Secretly, Signe had wept at the thought of parting; but when the day came and Soren, in company with a few neighbors, was about to leave for Skien to board a sailing vessel bound for America, she was brave.

"Here's something for you," she said and gave him a silk handkerchief and a simple, hand-carved, wooden lunch box.

He took them gravely and tried to thank her as he looked at her. She listened almost without hearing and said quietly: "If we only had enough money, I'd much rather go with you now. But as it is, we'll have to wait. So until then, goodbye, Soren."

In those days crossing the ocean was no pleasure trip; it required strength and courage and faith and patience. Days lengthened into weeks as the small vessels tossed ceaselessly. In foul weather passengers had to stay below in the stench and the vermin, trying in vain to quiet the whimpering of restless children. There was no food but what they had brought with them in quaint, hand-painted chests bearing the family name. Mothers, doling out bits of dried meat and hard flat bread, tried to encourage their children: "You must eat something. You need it to stay well and strong." The mothers needed to stay well, too.

In good weather the passengers would sit on deck. There for a time the sick could forget their trials as the sun warmed them into talk of summer at the mountain saeter, of the wild flowers, the fjords, their homes and dear ones. And with the comfort and cheer of good sailing weather, they would turn their thoughts from the homeland to speculate on the hopeful new world to which they were sailing.

Soren, who had only himself to look after, helped others keep up their courage. To be sure, he was so seasick the first few days that he wondered whether the Atlantic would get even his toenails. But as he recovered, he developed a philosophical approach. "See here," he grinned to his companions, "it could be worse. Think how much food you're saving. The time to feel bad is when you feel good again. Then you'll be hungry like me. Why," with a wink and a lowering of his voice, "right now I could easily eat our captain."

With his sea legs under him, Soren tucked in the sick, helped the mothers, played with the children, and cheered the men. But there were still long hours for dreaming of the future. One vision which appeared time and again he could not resist; he never tired of it. Yes, there it was— a picture of a farm, beautiful with trees and fields and rolling meadows, great flocks of sheep and herds of cattle,

*Crossing the
Atlantic, Soren
dreamed of
the future*

a money chest well stored with shining silver dollars—and
always Signe in his arms.

How disillusioning was the reality! Progress was slow
enough to make one despair. Day after day and week after
week the same endless ocean and the same wind, always
from the west. Soren chafed at the delay. He longed for
an end to this loafer's existence and fairly ached for a
chance to show America what a worker he was. He held
out his strong, work-hardened hands, threw back his shoul-
ders, drank in the salt sea air, and felt himself capable
of clearing a farm such as could not be found in all Telemark!

Surely it would not take long to make enough to send
for Signe. He would work and save so that she could have

every comfort. If he could only get there, so he could begin! He was sick of this endless waiting.

At last, after thirteen long weeks, the ship arrived at Quebec.

There was, of course, not one of the company who knew the language of the country, and they had barely the faintest notion of where they were going. They knew only that they were bound for a place called Wisconsin, where some people from their own part of Norway had already settled, and where glorious things were awaiting them. Where Wisconsin was, and whether it was a parish or a district as large as all Telemark, they knew not. They were herded along like a flock of sheep. At last, bewildered by all the new and strange things they had seen, and worn out by the long and exhausting journey, they stood on the wharf in Milwaukee.

Here many were met by relatives or friends who had been in the country a year or two. But these people did not look as if they had acquired their share of the great piles of riches said to be heaped up everywhere. On the contrary, they were more ragged than they had ever been in poor old Norway, and they were shaking with the ague, which had all but undone them.

Most of the newcomers were going to the homes of relatives or friends in Muskego, twenty miles southwest, where there had been a flourishing Norwegian settlement since 1839.

Anne Landsverk, one of Soren's fellow travelers, had a husband in America, and she was joining him. Shortly after their wedding he had sailed for America to make a home for her and had left her awaiting the birth of a child. Now she was coming with their infant son.

In Milwaukee, she looked around and her eyes filled with tears. No Ole was to be seen. Soren, who had been very helpful to her on the voyage, stood beside her, trying his best to comfort her. Then, lo and behold, there came Ole walking straight toward them! He took his wife's hand in his, their eyes met, and they trembled with happiness. Straightway she had to show him the baby and with quiet joy lifted the shawl from the little fellow's face.

"Do you think you would have recognized him as yours if you had found him somewhere?" she asked, as she smiled at her husband.

"That isn't a fair question," he laughed, as he looked up from his little son to his wife's shining eyes.

They were both so full of happiness that the world seemed a far better place than they had been able to imagine it for many a weary month.

Then Ole, who knew Soren well, greeted him heartily. Anne could not tell Ole often enough how good Soren had been to her, how he had helped her with the baby, and how he had kept up her courage during the terrible storm when she had been so frightened. Soren, she said, wasn't afraid of a thing.

Ole had brought a wagon with which to fetch his family home. Now, while he was busy loading the luggage and the oxen were eating some hay, Soren took a little walk uptown to see what he could see.

Milwaukee at that time was no large city; just the same, it was larger than Skien, with its 4,000 people—the town most like it of those Soren had seen in Norway. What impressed him most was that the Americans he saw did not really look much different from the people in Norway. They were about the same size and he would not have been surprised if they had spoken Norwegian. The houses, too, were not greatly unlike those he was accustomed to seeing. It was almost impossible for him to realize that he was really in a new world and that the wide ocean now rolled between Signe and him. How he wished he had brought her with him! But next he thought how perfectly wonderful it would be once to eat his fill. He had not done this for three months. His big, strong body craved other food than the dry fare he had lived on during the voyage.

He found his way back to Anne and Ole, who were now ready to start for Muskego. The plan was for him to go home with them for the present and later look for work. Anne took her place in the wagon and away they went. It was not a fast pace. Ole walked in front of the oxen with a long whip and shouted "Haw" and "Gee" and "Go long!" Anne was filled with admiration and confided to Soren, who was walking beside the conveyance, "Isn't it wonderful how well he speaks English already?"

The vehicle in which they rode is worth a second glance. It was a most primitive affair. Ole had made it all by himself and there was not a bit of iron in it. The wheels were four thick disks of wood which he had sawed from a tree trunk. In the middle of each disk a hole had been bored for the axle to pass through. The latter stuck out far enough to afford space for a hole into which a wooden peg was inserted to keep the wheel from slipping off. Resting on the axles was a rough wooden box with a board across it for a seat.

This crude contraption moved slowly and squeaked horribly. But it was inexpensive and, after all, not so bad on the swampy roads along which it had to travel. It was a true friend of the first settlers. It was called a trundle wagon.[1]

In this grand conveyance Ole and his company bumped along. At midnight they reached home—a little cabin nestling close to a beautiful grove, from which Ole had felled the trees and hewn the logs for his rude hut. Now the oxen were unharnessed and Ole, fumbling his way in, lit the lamp—a saucer of fat with a rag for a wick. Everything was crude and primitive; yet for Ole the hut was transformed into a palace as, perched on the bench, he gazed at Anne sitting on the edge of the bed with the child at her breast.

The very next day Soren began to help Ole with the task of clearing the woods, while Anne bustled about the house as if she had been there all her life.

Later in the summer Soren found work with a Yankee farmer named Newman who was operating on a big scale near Honey Creek, a few miles southwest of Waterford, Wisconsin. He soon proved to be unusually capable. He was used to hard work. When only a boy, he had lost both

[1] A trundle wagon or *kubberulle* may be seen in the Norwegian-American Historical Museum in Decorah, Iowa.

parents and ever since had had to earn his living. He was now a little past twenty, was strong and willing, and quickly became adept at swinging the cradle scythe. Many years later Mr. Newman used to say, "If I only had men like that Norwegian boy who worked for me before the war, harvesting machines would be superfluous."

"Yes, but he was an awfully big eater," Mrs. Newman would chime in.

"Well, if he ate for two," replied Mr. Newman, "he worked for two as well."

Soren stayed with these people two years. The first winter, since he was not so busy then as during the summer, he made a serious effort to learn English. As he never did things by halves, he went at this task with all his might. The teacher of the near-by public school, who lived with the Newmans, enjoyed talking to the big, blond immigrant and was willing to help him evenings with his language studies. For a time, too, with other grownups, he attended evening classes in the schoolhouse. Many poked fun at him because of his queer clothes and peculiar accent. As a rule he paid no attention, but if their comments became too personal, he occasionally responded with some pointed remarks of his own. If the merriment at his expense went too far, he sometimes tackled his tormentors in true Telemark style and sent them sprawling to the ground.

Since his pay the first year was only five dollars a month, he could save little. The second year, when his wages were higher, was better. And at last the time came when he could ask Mr. Newman to pay him, out of the wages due him, what he needed to buy an emigrant ticket. This he sent at once to Signe, who, on that little cotter's place in Tuddal, was waiting so eagerly. When this was done, Soren felt proud and happy.

But he knew he had to have a home for Signe when she came. In Muskego and the surrounding territory all public lands had been taken; but farther north to the west and northwest of Lake Winnebago in the so-called "Indian country," free land was still to be had. There, within a dense forest, a Norwegian settlement was springing up, later called Springville.[2] Some of Soren's acquaintances from the voyage had settled there; and now, in 1850, he set out to join them. The trip was not expensive, for he made it on foot, carrying his possessions with him in a sack. But he was dead tired when, at the end of the fourth day, he arrived at the home of Ole Kjeldalen, the leading citizen of Springville. Beside Kjeldalen, there were a number of other sturdy Norwegians living in the woods: Ole Skogen, and Lia, and Boerthe and Sigvat Halvorson, the last-named a relative of the man who was to become the first Norwegian farmer elected to the United States Congress. There were the Halling (who was so called because he came from Hallingdal), the Toten brothers, thus named because they came from Toten, Jens from Valders, and Hatlevik-Ole; and one who should have been mentioned first, namely, Klemmetsrud, a man known for his great "fear of the Lord." One of his sons, as is well known, was to become a leading clergyman of Hauge's Synod; his

---

[2] Springville represents the town of Winchester, about twelve miles west of Neenah.

daughter Liv married the even better-known lay preacher, Ole Maaseryg.

In this settlement our friend Soren Helgeson acquired 160 acres of land covered with a fine stand of oak. Right away he built a little cabin and began to clear the woods around it. The thought that he was building a home for Signe and himself gave him double strength, and he worked like a slave from dawn to dusk. Late at night, when the day's work was done, he would walk through the woods to Ole Kjeldalen's for a supper of cornmeal mush and milk. After that he would go to bed in the loft and fight mosquitoes until he was tired enough to sleep in spite of their bites.

The Kjeldalens sympathized with him, but found nothing unusual in his situation. They knew he was waiting for his betrothed. But Norwegians of their class are not demonstrative in their affections. Man and wife often live happily together for years without ever kissing each other. A husband returning home from an absence of several weeks is likely to say merely: "Well, how are you? Has everything gone well?" That is all there is to it. A boy both had known, who was only twelve years old, left home to be away two years. His mother only took his hand and said, "Goodbye, then, my boy." But after he was gone, she grieved until she became ill.

"It's been a long time for Soren," said Mrs. Kjeldalen.

"Oh, yes," said Ole, "but even the longest day ends."

One day word came that Signe, God bless her, had arrived in Muskego; what was better still, she was coming to Springville very soon with a family from that place.

21

Soren worked and longed and dreamed. One evening, when he returned to Kjeldalens, he sensed that something had happened. The wife, who sat milking, looked up and said, "Who do you think is here?" She would say no more. Soren, after hesitating a moment, started toward the cabin. His feet touched the ground but he felt as if he were floating on air.

He stepped into the tiny house, but no one was to be seen. Yes, someone was behind the door; and when he looked, there stood Signe, lovely and smiling, with tears in her eyes.

"How are you?" said Soren.

"How are you?" said Signe.

That was all. They stood gazing at each other, their hearts overflowing with joy. Signe beamed with pride at the tall, strong man who had acquired a blond beard since she last saw him. He, with hungry eyes, devoured her from top to toe. He could not look at her enough. She was beautiful; there was no denying it. Perhaps a little too buxom, but she had regular features—heavy dark hair, and eyes in which shone faith and love enough to spoil ten men. Soren's impulse was to clasp her to his heart, but he dared not; he must wait.

Now the family came in and listened spellbound to all that Signe had to tell about friends in the old country.

CHAPTER TWO

The first marriage in Bethel congregation

The next day Signe went with Soren to their future home and helped him put it in order. They wanted to be married at once. But unfortunately there was no minister within reach. Ole Kjeldalen agreed with Soren that the thing to do was go to an American justice of the peace to have a civil marriage or be "squared," that is, married by a squire. Signe disapproved of this plan. She was not sure that such a marriage would be valid. And Jens Knudson from Valders, who was a much-traveled man, spoke up with some authority: "Such 'squaring' is nothing more nor less than pure heathendom, anyway you look at it. You can bet your last dollar it would never have been permitted by our pastor back in Slidre. You mean to say you don't know who he is? Why, Harbitz is his name."[1]

This was indeed a problem. But it was soon solved, for not many days later word was sent from house to house that on the next Sunday a "really truly" Norwegian pastor was coming to Springville. He was to conduct services in Ole Kjeldalen's house and organize a congregation.

For the pioneers it was a great occasion indeed—that day when they were able to gather for the first time in their new homeland and hear a sermon by a Norwegian Lutheran pastor. Many of them had one or more children who had not "got a name," and now they brought them all along. Never before had the singing of hymns seemed so beautiful. All joined in. They sang in every key and did not keep time. Helga Knudson was three words behind the rest at the close of the first stanza, and she sang "Thee and Hea-ea-eaven" all alone.[2] But no one minded in the least. The only one who took offense was Klemmetsrud. He had long known that Helga was not a converted child of God and that her singing, therefore, was naught but sounding brass or a tinkling cymbal. The rest were happy; they felt as if they were back home in dear old Norway. And when Pastor Preus stepped forward and began his sermon, they were all ears and sometimes openmouthed, too. They could tell at once, of course, that he was a real pastor, because he wore the very same garb used by clergymen in

[1] Georg Prahl Harbitz (1802-89), clergyman and politician, was a member of the Storting, 1836-69 and president of it, 1851-69.

[2] Helga Knudson, in real life, was Ragnhild Juv.

24

The first pastor comes to the settlement

the old country. His "state," namely, the black gown and white ruff, was proof that he was a "state" clergyman and just as good as if he belonged to the state church.[3]

In simple, heart-warming words, he told his hearers that in this New World they could not live by bread alone, any

[3] In the original, *stas*, meaning finery, is confused by the people with *stats*, meaning state. The two words would be pronounced practically alike. A clergyman of the church of Norway wore a white ruff of the Elizabethan type.

more than in the Old World; and he admonished them, above all, to preserve the faith of their fathers.

The infants who were to be baptized howled distressingly. The room was like an oven, and as the poor little things had been dressed by their mothers in layer after layer of clothes, it is not to be wondered at that they cried. Since the pastor could not stop up his ears and at the same time perform the rite of baptism, he had no choice but to make the best of the situation.

These parents had been but a short time in America, yet they had already learned that it would not do to give their children honest Norwegian names. They were afraid the "Yankees" might not be able to pronounce them. Ingeborg, therefore, became Isabelle; Kari, Katie; and even a good name like Sigrid was changed to Sarah or Sally; one poor little boy who was to be named for his grandfather, Harald, was left to rejoice in the name of Horace.

When the service was over and some food had been served, the men assembled to consider organizing a congregation. Pastor Preus explained the procedures to be followed under the free-church conditions prevailing in this country, which were so different from those of the state church in Norway.

Yes, everyone was much in favor of organizing. For, of course, they had to have a pastor to christen and confirm their children; otherwise they would simply revert to heathendom. Jens Knudson wondered whether baptizing and such like was necessary in America, where there was so much land which did not belong to any parish, and where, actually, people could be found who had never been baptized but still had names just the same, wherever in the world they might have got them from. But he did not dare express such thoughts aloud. He merely hinted that he would like very much to know what Pastor Harbitz would have thought of the whole business. And there was Nils Klemmetsrud, who had been influenced by the religious revival of western Norway. He was a very pious man in both conduct and speech, especially in speech; and during the sermon strong doubts arose in him as to whether Pastor Preus really had ever been converted. Why, in his sermon the pastor had not even shed a tear! And besides, he had read part of it from a manuscript. It certainly looked as if he relied solely upon his book learning.

Klemmetsrud, moreover, was suspicious of all these state-church clergymen and would have preferred asking Elling Eielsen to come.[4] But since he knew that no one would agree with him, he thought it best to go along with the others. All the men present now signed a document which declared that they had united to form the Bethel Norwegian Lutheran Congregation of Springville, Wisconsin.

At one point the whole project was within a hair's breadth of stranding. It had first been proposed to name the organization Hitterdal Congregation, as most of the members were from Hitterdal in Norway. At this suggestion things grew lively. Jens Knudson was from Valders; he was a small, lame man with a stubborn disposition, full of whims and superstitions. He had somehow strayed over

---

[4] Elling Eielsen, who began his work as a layman among the Norwegian emigrants, was the first ordained Norwegian-American Lutheran pastor (1843).

into Springville from the new Valders settlement near Manitowoc, and was the only Valders man in the community; accordingly, he was usually called Valdrisen, that is, the man from Valders.

He now declared that neither he nor Helga, his wife, would join a congregation named Hitterdal. He was backed up by Klemmetsrud, who felt that this was a matter of conscience. He did not consider Hitterdal a Christian title, and he moved that the congregation be called Bethel, a name dear to all children of God. Jens seconded the motion. To be sure, he did not know exactly what "Bethel" meant, not having heard the word before. But he was able to grasp that at least the name held no hidden offense against him, a Valders man. And certainly the people from Valders were every bit as good as the people from Telemark. They should just have heard the preaching of Pastor Harbitz, who certainly did not need to take a back seat for anyone in all Norway. He could have had his choice of any parish in the land, but Valders was good enough for him.

For the sake of peace, then, they agreed to call the congregation "Bethel," although Preus was actually so lacking in piety as to tell Klemmetsrud straight to his face that it was no sin to call a congregation "Hitterdal."

That reef having been cleared, the congregation was established, with Kjeldalen, one of the Toten brothers, and Klemmetsrud as trustees. In electing these men, attention had been given to geographical origin, for they represented respectively, Telemark in southern Norway, Toten in central Norway, and Stavanger on the west coast.

28

It was a bitter disappointment to Jens Knudson that he was not elected. But he soon swallowed his vexation, consoling himself by thinking that the others certainly had no better prospects of getting to heaven than he, especially not that fellow from Toten who, it could be proved, was given to drinking and profanity and, besides, was so addicted to card playing that it had become proverbial. There was a story that, one night not long before this, his oxen had come home from town alone while he lay sleeping by the roadside. And when a couple of neighbors found him and tried to wake him up, he answered, half-asleep, "If I'd known you were going to play like that, I'd certainly have put on the queen." If such a man could be elected trustee, then Jens certainly would have been good enough for the position, too.

For the time being, the new congregation did not feel able to support a minister, but it was promised that Pastor Duus would visit the parish three or four times a year.

After the services and the congregational meeting and when nearly everyone had left, our friend Soren Helgeson went over to Pastor Preus and asked if he might speak to him.

"Why, yes," said the pastor, "certainly. What do you wish?"

"Well, I just wanted to know if the pastor would be good enough to help me out in a little matter; I have thought of making a change." At first Preus thought that he had before him a penitent sinner who wished to change his way of life, but he soon realized that it was quite another matter. Everything was quickly explained; the Kjeldalens assured the pastor that all was as it should be. Then Soren and Signe stepped forward and were married.

Ole Kjeldalen, with his own hands, had made a small bench for the occasion. Covered with a sheet, it served as a kneeler. So nothing was lacking. The only hitch was that Signe answered, "No," when asked if she could truthfully say that she had not given any other man now living a matrimonial vow which would be a hindrance to this marriage. But after the question had been properly explained to her, she answered, "Yes."

In the evening the newlyweds went to their home, and Soren was proud as a king.

CHAPTER THREE

A son and heir

The home to which Soren Helgeson brought his young bride was humble, indeed. It lay deep in the dark forest with only a small clearing around it. And even on this small spot the great black stumps were still standing, awaiting the time when they would have rotted sufficiently to be pulled out with oxen and a log chain. The house, like all others in the settlement, was built of great oak logs. It had only one room, with a loft above it. The furniture consisted of a couple of homemade benches, a table likewise homemade, a cookstove, and a bed. The last-named stood in a corner under the ladder going up to the loft.

Soren and Signe

In the floor was a trap door, leading to a little hole in the ground which served as a cellar. Near the door to the outside, nailed to the wall, was a low shelf on which stood a washbowl with a piece of yellow soap beside it. Close to the beams was another shelf, on which lay nails, auger, broad axe, and other tools. And over by the stove was still another shelf for kitchen utensils. Clothes hung on the wall or were folded away in a chest at the foot of the bed. On the table lay a Bible brought by Signe from Norway, and another book entitled *The Saints' Eternal Rest*, both of which had to be moved to the bed when the table was to be set.

This was all its grandeur; but the two who possessed it also had faith and hope and—what is greater—love; so they had enough. Moreover, they were capable and industrious and soon began to get ahead. In addition, since Soren was a well-informed man who took pride in learning the ways of his new country, he soon became one of the leading men of the community. When the township was organized, he was elected justice of the peace in spite of his youth. Little by little, he became a kind of legal adviser to the neighbors, writing out their notes, drawing up their deeds and other papers. Honest in all his dealings, he was respected by all.

The winter after the wedding, Signe, poor girl, was not always well. Apparently she could not relish her food, especially mornings. This was not strange, considering that meals consisted of pork and potatoes, except for supper, when there was corn-meal mush. Sometimes, when Soren came home, he found her in tears. As spring advanced, she felt better; but by midsummer she was no longer able to help with the outdoor work. One evening, as she stood with her arms folded beneath her breast, watching her husband hoe potatoes, she suddenly felt ill and said, "Soren, you'd better get Helga Knudson." Soren helped her into the cabin and ran as fast as he could to Knudson's. Because he arrived in such haste, the knowing Helga was quick to sense what was up. She was ready in a moment and followed him, carrying a bottle of camphorated whiskey.

Helga was the only real midwife in the settlement. There was Kari Sandbakken, to be sure; she occasionally had had the presumption to officiate in that capacity; but Helga could not for the life of her see how anyone who knew how easily things might go wrong could entrust herself to such a wooden-fisted person's handling.

Helga got a great deal of satisfaction out of her work and was proud of her ability. She was never so completely happy as when she could sit with a full saucer of coffee balanced on her finger tips and relate all the circumstances of the last case at which she had officiated. She had a mother's heart for all the many children she had helped into the world. When they grew up, she gave them good advice, always defending her right to do so by saying, "You know, I was the first one who saw you; I welcomed you when you came into the world."

In the present case all went well, although Soren suddenly became frightened and was ready to run out on Helga; she really had to scold him for being such a poor help—great big good-for-nothing that he was! But Helga managed and Signe was delivered of a son.

The next day, after Helga had found a girl to take care of Signe, Soren went back to the potato patch. He was somewhat more thoughtful than before, and would often stop and gaze into space. Many times, he had to tiptoe to the door to see if Signe and the boy were asleep.

The news of the event traveled fast, for Helga at once found necessary errands to the neighbors and told them that Signe had been blessed with a son. He was, she said, a big, strong boy, although she thought he had come a few days too early; this was due, without question, to the fact that Signe had been frightened one evening when Klemmetsrud had come into the house when she was alone. A little tipsy, he had been on his way home from town and had begun to weep over the lost condition of Soren's soul. Signe had had to exert herself beyond her strength to get him to go home.

The women of the neighborhood were so kind that at first it was hard for Signe to regain her strength. Every day a number of them would pay her a visit. Each one would bring a bowl of cream mush, as it was called; and some of the best-intentioned also brought home-brewed ale. Then they would sit and sit, urging the weak mother to eat, while they entertained her by telling the details of their own similar experiences.

All this kindness nearly put the poor woman in her grave. Of course, the least she could do was taste the mush each one brought. And mush is tempting fare. It tastes extremely good, but one has eaten too much long before one is ready to stop. And the richer the mush is, the better, presumably. In any event, it had to be so rich that it could "butter itself" in the kettle. And even then a little butter was added to it, and the whole sprinkled with brown sugar and cinnamon.

Signa had a strong constitution, however, and recovered in spite of all the kindness shown her. Soon she was up and around again, attending to her household duties. When she and Soren were alone evenings, all sorrow was forgotten as, in tranquil joy, they gazed at the boy at Signe's breast lustily taking his fill. Never had Soren seen so lovely a sight. He would gently touch the baby's face and stroke the mother's hair; doing so, he felt himself to be the richest man in all the world. Now he would really get down to work. He would take good care of Signe. He would never say an unkind word to her. And when the boy grew up, he would go to school and be educated for the ministry or the law, or something equally great; no one would dream that he was the son of a Norwegian lad who had come to America without a dollar in his pocket.

Soon word reached them that, by a fortunate turn of events, Pastor Duus was coming to conduct services; thus Soren and Signe were able to have their boy christened. He was named Halvor. Helga Knudson, who had brought him into the world, was his godmother and carried him at the service—an honor which she always treasured greatly. She was godmother of nearly all the children in the community.

As was customary, Soren and Signe had a christening party. After the service a number of the neighbors went home with them and were regaled with cream mush. As the evening wore on, more and more people came—the latter uninvited. Anyone might come to a christening, with the understanding, of course, that he bring a gift for the child—an article of apparel or a sum of money, according to his means.

The men sat outside against the wall of the cabin and, as usual, it was Jens Knudson who led the conversation. He was dreadfully ill-informed and had the credulity that goes with ignorance. However, his respect for book learning was prodigious. He held Soren, in particular, in the highest esteem because Soren already could read and write English. Jens vowed that if he had as much book learning as Soren, he certainly would not keep slaving away like an ordinary farmer. He would go to the city and make piles of money. Jens, to be sure, did have considerable native sagacity, had dabbled a little in everything, and knew remedies for all sorts of ailments, particularly those of cattle, his pet medicine being oil of spike, in which he had a faith that was actually pathetic. During his sojourn in the Manitowoc area he had seen a good deal of the Indians and could tell many strange things about them. He did not like their way of living, yet always excused them by saying, "But, of course, they are really descended from the heathen, you know."

He firmly believed that pastors had the "black book" in their possession, and could do whatever they chose, and that there was nothing under the sun they did not know.

On this Sunday evening Jens was really in his element. Among the yarns he told was this:

"It was the year just before I went to America, and it happened that another boy and I were digging a well; and way down deep in the earth we found a little box; and in this box was a little bottle; and in this bottle was a little animal about as big as my little finger. We took the bottle to the pastor—Pastor Harbitz it was—and asked him what in heaven's name that animal might be. Well, Harbitz sent the bottle in to Christiania; and it was not long before it came back with strict orders from the government and the professors for God's sake not to open it but to bury it just where we found it."

"Well, what in the world was in that bottle, then?" asked Pastor Duus.

"Oh, you know what was in the bottle, all right; of course you know, for you're a pastor."

"No, really I don't. Now just go ahead and tell us."

"Oh, you know all right. Why, there was a little devil's imp in that bottle. And I can tell you that Pastor Harbitz made us bury it, and quick, too. And that was just a year before I left for America."

Later in the evening, when the preacher had left, the fun began. Hans Skogen, who had brought his fiddle, sat down to tune it while the floor was cleared for dancing. Klemmetsrud suggested they would do better to give thought to their immortal souls, but no one paid the slightest attention to him. As soon as the floor was cleared, the men, one by one, walked over to the bed and laid their christening gifts upon it. A few who wanted to show what great fellows they were gave as much as five dollars. One dollar was the rule, however. Then the young folks began to dance. Signe herself had to dance the first number to show that she was as well as ever; that was the custom.

Meantime most of the men sat outside, drinking and singing ballads. Jens knew one he called "The Ballad of Valders," and it was very well received. The hero of the song, who had recently come to America, told how he had proved to the Yankees the prowess of the men from Valders, and thereby had won honor and glory. Next o'd Hatleviken, in his singsong Sogning dialect, contributed a ballad. Then there was another, in which all could join, as it had been composed by a local rhymester and described the community and its people.

While the ballads were being sung and while the dancing within the house was growing noisier, trouble was brewing outside among the men. Many of them had brought alcohol with them from home which they mixed with the home-brewed beer; and as they grew a little tipsy, they began to taunt one another. Among those present was Ole Findreng. There was a rumor that he had once stolen a whetstone and a clevis from a plow in a neighbor's field, and for this reason he had been nicknamed Whetstone-Ole. Aanun Strand could not resist picking a quarrel with Ole by repeatedly dropping covert remarks to the effect that usually a clevis was needed to hook up a plow and, likewise, that a whetstone was a very useful article. Under a pretense of friendliness, and with an innocent air, he asked: "What do you think, Ole? Do you think a whetstone will float in water?"

In an instant they were in the thick of a fight. Women screamed and begged the men to stop them before either was hurt. Soren got a grip on the belligerents and told them to behave themselves; when this did no good, he sent them sprawling to the ground in opposite directions.

Whetstone-Ole had fared the worse of the two and was bleeding profusely. But after he had washed and had put down another drink, he swore he would have made short work of Aanun if only it had not been too dark to see what he was doing.

At last, after all had left and Soren and Signe were in bed, Signe said, "I don't think such parties are any fun."

"You're certainly right about that," replied Soren. "But you know how it is with the first child. One has to have a party then. But this is the end of the parties. I'll never have such a row in this house again."

Then Signe said a little hesitantly, "Soren, tell me, you're not getting fond of strong drink, are you?"

"No," said Soren, "I'm not. Perhaps I did have a little too much tonight. But this is the last time. I promise you that, Signe."

And that promise he kept.

CHAPTER FOUR

Sorrow

Soren Helgeson had been fortunate in getting a good piece of land, but it was a tremendous task to clear it. As he was incredibly industrious, however, the clearing around the house grew steadily larger, and it looked as if his dream of wealth would be realized. In between the many oak stumps he planted potatoes and corn, and sowed oats and a little wheat. He prospered, and he and his wife were happy and thankful that they had settled in this new land. The longing for home which had caused them so much pain the first year or two had gradually worn away. But now Soren received a blow from which he never recovered.

When little Halvor was two years old and Signe again was with child, Signe one evening was so badly gored by one of the oxen that Soren had to carry her into the house and lay her on the bed. He rushed off to get Helga Knudson; when he returned, he found Signe in great pain. The moment Helga arrived, the child was born; but Helga's practiced eye quickly saw that it could not live. So she got a bowl of water and gave the babe a private baptism. Not for anything in the world would she have burdened her conscience by allowing a child to depart this life unbaptized. This had happened once when she was present; she had suffered much on account of it, for Klemmetsrud had made a point of letting her know that it was doubtful whether there would be forgiveness for such a sin.

Helga had not been mistaken; during the night the child died. When Signe, in a faint voice, asked to see it and they had to tell her that it had been taken to its heavenly home, her only reply was that she would soon be going there, too. She lay perfectly quiet until morning. Then she began to murmur the Lord's Prayer aloud.

"You aren't going to leave me, are you?" asked Soren; he stood by her bed and his eyes never left her.

She asked for little Halvor. They took him up from the cradle and let his mother caress him. Then she grasped Soren's hand and drew a deep sigh; after a short while, another; then Helga said gently and solemnly that it was all over. That was all. It has happened many times, and it hurt Soren He'geson just as much as it would have hurt the president of the United States, only people do not say so much about it.

Soren stood, bowed down over the bed. Then he straightened up and went out to the chopping block. He took the broadax which lay there and went over to the barn wall where the vicious ox stood chewing his cud, unaware of what was to happen. One blow between the eyes felled him to the ground. Soren struck him again a couple of times to make sure he would never rise again. Then laying the ax away, he went in, picked up little Halvor in his arms, sat down on the bench, and began to breathe so heavily that Helga was frightened. The only comfort she could offer was to say that Signe's time must have come.

Soren sat awhile as if turned to stone, then got a grip on himself and asked Helga in a resigned voice to do whatever needed to be done. Word was sent for old Kari Sandbakken, who always assisted on such occasions.

Jens came and helped Soren make the coffin; and his son Knud was sent to invite the neighbors to the funeral.

They came in the forenoon, quietly and solemnly. It was customary for everyone to have dinner before proceeding to the cemetery. As the table was small and the guests many, dinner took a long time. The guests were all too modest to come forward for the first serving; one by one, they had to be persuaded to do so. When the most prominent men at last were seated, old Hatleviken, who was the parish deacon and always acted as master of ceremonies at funerals, took a position at one end of the table and sang, as slowly as he could, the first stanza of "Who Knows How Soon My Life May End?"

The old man had been precentor in the church at Lyster in Norway, and he followed the old custom scrupulously.

When he had finished the stanza, he said, "Now that you are seated, my friends, let us all say the customary table prayer, 'The eyes of all wait upon Thee, O Lord.'"

When they had repeated this silently, or had pretended to do so, he said, "Please help yourselves, my friends, to the meal that has been prepared for you."

Then he kept an eye on them; when he saw that all had finished eating, he said, "If you are all satisfied, my good people, you must not forget to thank God for the meal. Let each one give thanks in the customary way by repeating: 'Thank the Lord, for He is good.'"

When this had been done, he continued: "I hope you have all made out a meal, my friends. Now let us thank our friends and neighbors who were kind enough to bring the provisions for this meal. A word or a handclasp serves equally well."

All stood up and, shaking hands with their neighbors to the right and left, thanked them for the meal. The table was then cleared in all haste and set for the next group. At this setting and those that followed, old Hatlevik was not quite so particular about following the rules in every detail; even so, it was almost evening before the dinner was over.

The coffin in which Signe lay with the babe at her side was placed on a wooden bench in the middle of the room and they made ready to start. Ole Kjeldalen, the only one of the settlers affluent enough to own horses, drew up before the door. The coffin was carried out, with the precentor heading the procession, singing a hymn. By virtue of his office he seated himself next to Ole Kjeldalen and the

Soren felt as if his heart went down with the coffin

procession started—the wagon in the lead and the mourners following afoot, for the distance was not great. Soren walked directly behind the wagon.

On an elevation in one corner of Kjeldalen's farm, land had been set aside for a cemetery, with the plan that in time a church should be built at this location. A few graves were already there, marked by wooden crosses painted black. The coffin was lifted from the wagon and lowered while they sang "No Better Journey Can I Take Than That Which Leads Me Home to God." Soren felt as if his heart had been torn from him and went down with the coffin and remained there when the grave was filled in.

Ole Kjeldalen stepped up and invited Soren to go home with him. But Soren declined with thanks, saying that he

45

preferred to be by himself; slowly he walked toward his cabin, his mind filled with memories of Signe's love and loyalty and courage. On reaching home, he sat down with little Halvor, and although the boy was too young to understand, began to tell him what they both had lost. How good and loving she had always been, God bless her! With pain he recollected that once he had wounded her by saying that she had been careless with the food. How hard it seemed that she should die just when the burden of poverty was being lifted and he was about to provide a more comfortable home! It was a bitter thing, too, that she had had to be buried without the presence of a minister to express the Christian hope of resurrection. Soren was sensible enough to know that Signe rested quite as well without this; nevertheless, it would have been a comfort if Pastor Duus had been near enough to be sent for.

Mrs. Sandbakken, who had undertaken to keep house for him temporarily, now came and began to get supper. And then Klemmetsrud came. He sat down and heaved a great sigh, which was supposed to signify sympathy. Then he started to exhort Soren not to take his loss too hard, but to resign himself to God's will and comfort himself with the thought that perhaps Signe's soul was saved.

The last remark was too much. Soren grew indignant and told Klemmetsrud that no comfort was needed on that score. He had not the slightest doubt that Signe had gone straight home to God. Then he asked Klemmetsrud to leave him in peace.

Klemmetsrud on his way home grew thoughtful and began to have doubts about the state of Soren's soul. But

Soren sat a long time alone, brooding darkly. Then light came to him and, smiling an almost happy smile, he undressed Halvor and told him that Mother and baby sister were now with God in heaven and were happy.

CHAPTER FIVE

Halvor grows up

Soren became inordinately fond of his boy—his dearest remembrance of Signe. Wherever he went, the child had to go with him; and little by little, as Halvor grew, a warm comradeship developed between them. It was not to be wondered at, for each was all the other had. To help about the house and farm, Soren brought in a childless couple who had just come from Norway. With them on the place he could have left Halvor home when he had an errand to one or another of the neighbors. But he could not stand to be separated from the boy, even for a short time, unless it was absolutely necessary. If he happened to be working alone in a field, he would hurry home to look after Halvor.

Very early the boy heard all about the mother whom he had forgotten—how beautiful and kind she had been; and he learned to think of her as a white-robed angel who was sitting in heaven with her little child in her arms and with her gentle eyes watching him and his father, wherever they might be. He learned that it would grieve her if he did anything wrong, and not for anything in the world would he have caused her sorrow. With his love and admiration for his big, strong father there was mingled a kind of pity, too, for he could see that for some reason his father was not a happy man. To be sure, he was always kind and would talk of many things with his son. But otherwise he was almost always silent and often sat a long time brooding.

So time passed until Halvor was six years old and started to attend the district school. At this time there came a change in the household which the boy at first could not understand. The couple who had lived so long in Soren's house moved out because the husband had secured some land for himself; and now Soren engaged a daughter of Kari Sandbakken to keep house for him. Halvor did not like her; she always made him feel that he was in her way. But for some reason or other Soren and she often sat talking together; and one day, while the boy was in school, they went over to Kjeldalen's, where Pastor Nils O. Brandt just then happened to be stopping on his way to the "Indian country." When Halvor came home, he found his father and Anne sitting at the table, dressed in their best and looking self-conscious. Soren called the boy over and told him that hereafter he must call Anne "Mother." Halvor did not wish to do that. He had never heard of anyone having more than one mother, and his mother was in heaven; that he knew very well. In the evening, when he was to go to bed, he was shown a place by himself up in the loft. He could not imagine what it was all about, and would have felt utterly wretched and forsaken had not his father came up and talked to him until he fell asleep.

In a short time, however, he was awakened and frightened nearly out of his wits. Pandemonium had suddenly broken out all around the house. Having heard tales of Indians, he thought a band of savages must have come to kill him. There were hoarse yells and shouts, mingled with the clang of cowbells and tin pans. Occasionally a shot rang out.

The fact was that Soren had been married without announcing it previously, and this was the punishment. The howling mob had come to "shivaree" the couple. Soren went out and, rather mildly, asked these disturbers of the peace to go home, only to be told that they would not think of doing that until he had treated them to drinks all around. This Soren flatly refused to do, adding that for one thing he did not have any brandy in the house. The horrible din started again. Some young fellows succeeded in getting a window open and loosed a pig into the house. Others amused themselves by uprooting some young apple trees which had just got a nice start. Still others took Soren's wagon apart and hid the several pieces here, there, and everywhere. Not until past midnight did they tire of the fun; and not until Soren, to humor the crowd, appeared in the doorway with his bride and told them that if they left he would thank them very much, but if they did not, he would shoot, did the rowdies finally depart.

This foolish custom, which was called "shivareeing," was much practiced in those days, especially at weddings which the public disapproved for one reason or other, or when some well-to-do person got married without giving a party commensurate with his means or standing in life. Fortunately, this idiocy has now almost gone out of fashion.

Halvor was jealous of his new mother. What right had she to take his place? He soon grew used to calling her "Mother"; but like her, he could not. The first time she punished him for some minor offense, he became so angry that he threw himself flat on the ground and kicked and screamed. When Soren arrived on the scene, he said mildly to the boy, "If you do not want to grieve your father, you must mind your mother." Then he went into the house and said sternly; "You may as well understand this, Anne, that you must be good to Halvor. If he needs a spanking, I'll give it to him myself."

From this time on Halvor was left more and more to himself. His father seemed to go to town very often; when he came home, he always talked about the Civil War, which had just broken out, intimating that he, too, was thinking of going to fight for the abolition of slavery.

In the summer, however, Halvor's life was a rather pleasant one, in spite of his loneliness. Then he was not allowed to stay indoors; he would have been in Anne's way.

In the morning he first had to drive the cattle down the runway to the "slough land" where they grazed. In this meadow there was a little pool in which he could wade and catch tadpoles. Once he caught one that had just begun to sprout legs. He carried it home; when he learned that tadpoles turned into frogs, he became more interested in the creatures than ever. Then, too, he came to know all the birds' nests around his home. He knew exactly how many eggs there were in each and followed their hatching with fatherly interest. Snakes he did not like and he had many a battle with them. Among the first things he had learned from Helga Knutson, his godmother, was that snakes should be killed, because it was a snake that had induced Eve to eat of the forbidden fruit in Paradise. While he was still very young, he had learned the trick of taking a snake by the tail and cracking it—just as his father cracked the whip over the backs of his oxen—so that the snake's head flew off. Another favorite sport was the game of seesawing toads. A board was laid across a block, the toad put on one end of the board, and the other end struck so hard with a club that the poor creature was thrown high into the air.

But Helga, who gave him his first instruction in the Christian faith, soon taught him that it was a sin to seesaw toads. He received other religious instruction from her as well, such as that it was a sin to whistle, to walk backwards, or to whittle on Sunday. To whistle—that was to call upon the Evil One; to walk backwards was the same as to wish one's mother in hell. Halvor, nevertheless, occasionally ventured to do these things when no one could see or hear him; but he suffered terribly from pangs of conscience afterward. The most dangerous of all these practices was to whittle on Sunday; for Helga had told him repeatedly that if he did so, all the shavings he had cut off would be burned on his hand in the next world.

Since Halvor was a very conscientious little boy and did not enjoy the prospect of having his hand burned, he was exceedingly careful not to whittle on Sunday. If at times he absolutely had to have something to whittle on that day, he would first select a lonely spot and then carefully cut off the stick with his knife, making the shavings as thin and few in number as possible. These he would gather up very carefully and either scatter to the winds or trample into the ground, reasoning that if God now should find them and burn them on his hand, he would just have to stand the pain; at any rate there would not be enough of them to make a big fire.

On weekdays, when he had driven the cattle to the pasture, his next task was to trudge to the schoolhouse, a little log building right by the main road. In school Halvor did very well, and before long he could tell his father a great many strange things that the latter had never heard of. Of an evening the boy would often sit outdoors alone and think about George Washington, who was the Father of all America; and then he would think of his own father who, he knew, was much stronger and wiser than Washington. Or he would gaze through the openings in the woods at the many pillars of smoke rising from as many farms, all of them from fires kindled to keep the mosquitoes away while the cows were being milked. Sometimes he would chase the fireflies that flashed here and there among the trees. And suddenly he would put his ear to the ground to see if he could hear his father's wagon coming back from town. It could be heard at a great distance, for the road was uneven and some parts of it had been built by laying great logs side by side over the swampy stretches. Great was the joy when his father arrived. There was always a treat for the boy—either an apple or some candy. Just think! On his birthday Halvor got a pencil and a little pocketknife, the edge of which his father had filed down a little for safety's sake. Halvor liked it none the less for that, and he hid it and the pencil carefully in a crack in the wall near his bed in the loft.

The first Christmas after his new mother came was an unusually happy one for Halvor. It was not that Anne had grown more fond of him. Quite the contrary; she was cross and irritable. But, as if to compensate for this, his father was always thinking of new ways to please him and show him that they two at least were as good friends as ever. Thus, on Christmas Eve Halvor was allowed to hang up his stockings to see if anything would find its way into them during the night. He woke up many times wondering what there might be, and early in the morning he scrambled out of bed to look. Good gracious! How happy he was! His stockings were full of cakes and candy, and beside them stood a tin horse and a pair of boots, the toes of which were tipped with copper to make them last longer. His father told him to go over and thank his mother, too. He did this. She commented that it was remarkable how much his father could afford when it was a question of something for this youngster. "Well, now," replied Soren, "I guess I can afford to spend a few pennies at Christmastime. After all, it's my own money, isn't it?"

When spring came, Soren again began to talk about going to the war. A great number of the neighbors had gone and he felt it his duty to do the same. It would be a disgrace he thought, to remain quietly at home. But Anne complained, pleading that he could not possibly leave her in her present condition. There was nothing he could do but resign himself to staying home.

It seemed to Halvor that at this time Anne was much given to grumbling. She had a soft, delicate voice, which flowed on indefinitely in the same monotonous tone; her volubility was utterly amazing.

"Well, I don't say I know very much, but I do say this now, that as far as I understand, according to my judgment, I do think this—and I realize I don't know very much, that I will admit—but just the same it seems to me in my humble opinion, so far as I can judge, that it cannot be right of you, Soren, to think of going to the war now; you must in any event first wait until my time is over, for I seem to feel within me that you will soon be a widower again; then you can go where you will and take your boy with you that you are so fond of, although I really can't see that he is any better than other boys except at creating a disturbance, but not that I know much about it, but there is this much you may as well know, that if you leave me now, you are committing a great sin."

Soren listened patiently until she was through.

56

"Yes, yes, Anne, of course I'll stay home, so there's no need to say anything more about it. And you'll see that you're not going to die because of what's coming, either. Such things, of course, have happened many times before. And anyway, it certainly isn't Halvor's fault."

Well, then, it was the same old story. One evening Halvor had permission to go to Jens Kundson's to stay overnight, something he considered a great treat, it was always so pleasant there. Whenever he was there of an evening and ate mush with them, Helga and Jens always let him scrape the kettle. Moreover, Jens had a half-grown son named Knud who already knew how to use tobacco and swear when his father was not around; Halvor naturally looked up to him with exceedingly great admiration.

When Halvor came down from the loft the next morning, Helga told him that he might run home now. He had got a little sister, she said; they had found her under the root of an old oak stump not far from the house. Halvor fairly flew home and came into the house all out of breath.

"Father, is it true that you found a baby girl?"

"Hush, you mustn't make any noise. Mother is sick."

Halvor quieted down at once. Everything seemed strange in the house. In the corner lay Anne, pale and weak; and over by the stove sat her mother, old Mrs. Sandbakken, with a bundle on her lap.

"Come here, Halvor, and you can see your little sister."

Halvor grew fond of the baby at once—fonder than he had ever been of anyone in the world. He asked if she were alive, but needed no answer, for at that moment she uttered a cry that made him jump. She was the prettiest thing he had ever seen. And to think that they found her under a stump! That was the most interesting part of it all. Yet he thought it was tedious and very awkward that his mother should be sick just then when her help was so much needed to take care of the baby.

"I wonder," thought he, "if there are any more to be found?" He got a spade and began quietly to dig under an oak stump near the barn. Finding nothing, he concluded that he would have to be content with the one baby they had.

After Anne was up and around again, Halvor would watch his chance, when she was outside, to go to the cradle and look at his little sister. What fun it was to put his index finger into her little hand and feel her tiny fingers grasp it and hold it fast! Or when she held up one little foot, to take one toe at a time and say what he had learned from the Kjeldalen children, "This one stole, this one carried away, this one broke the lock, this one tattled, and this one got all the blame!"

The little one could not be baptized until late in the fall, for the congregation had no regular pastor yet. It had to get along with a few visits each year from Preus or Ottesen or Brandt, or some other of the tireless pioneer pastors who, with almost unparalleled courage amid unbelievable privations and hardships, traveled from place to place in the woods, organizing congregations and reminding the newcomers that the dominion of the God they had worshipd in Norway extended even here. These men—Preus, Koren, Larsen, Stub, Ottesen, Brandt, Muus, and others have done our people a service whose value can never be measured. They suffered hardships like good soldiers; and they brought light and happiness to the humble pioneer homes scattered far and wide.

Soren and Anne's girl was all of four months old when Klemmetsrud dropped in one evening to tell them that Pastor Brandt was to conduct services next Sunday in the schoolhouse. So long a period had elapsed since the child's birth that the parents had had ample time to disagree about her name. At last, however, it was decided that she should be named for Soren's mother, who was called Guri. She therefore was christened Jenny. Jenny was considered finer, naturally, than Guri.

The day Jenny was christened was a red-letter day for Halvor. He went to church with his parents and, although he was only seven years old, he was so impressed that he was not himself for months. For the sermon was about Judgment Day. So vividly was this day pictured that he thought he saw the whole world on fire and heard the shrieks of the doomed as they were thrown into outer darkness. And the pastor said that that dreadful day was coming soon. "It is coming soon. We are living in the last days." He repeated this several times. By "soon" Halvor thought, of course, he meant in a day or two. It did not occur to him to doubt the truth of what the pastor had spoken. Nor could he imagine that the pastor meant anything longer than a week or two at the most. He was terribly frightened.

He also recalled something he had heard his godmother, Helga Knudson, read from a little book, which to her was a dear devotional book and quite as reliable as the Bible itself. It was the story of a young girl in Norway who had been caught up and taken to the evil place. There she had seen great numbers of the damned in a huge kettle of boiling water. They stretched up their arms and sometimes succeeded in getting hold of the rim of the kettle and tried to pull themse'ves out. But then the Evil One himself came with a red-hot poker which he passed around the rim so that they had to drop their hold. The book also related that some of these doomed ones, judging by the size of their hands, were not more than seven years old. From this circumstance Halvor concluded that those under seven were safe. Unfortunately he was already over seven, and he had many times whistled, walked backwards, and whittled on Sunday, and sinned in other ways. Yet he felt sure that his father would be able to take care of him, if only Judgment Day would come when they were together. But what if it should come when his father was away or he himself was in school? The very thought terrified him so that he was almost sick. It was all his parents could do to make him go to school. He secured a seat near a window so that he could look out every once in a while for any signs that Judgment Day was approaching. He imagined it would come like a storm, and he resolved that the moment he saw anything that looked ominous, he would dash for home, in spite of anything the teacher might say or do, so that he could be with his father and mother and little sister; she, at least, was sure to get to heaven. In a pinch he might even hang on to her and thus get to go along to the same place.

*Helga had
warned Halvor
against whittling
on Sunday*

Strangely enough, one day after another passed, and Judgment Day never came. A couple of times it looked as if it might be close at hand, and Halvor grew pale and asked his father if the world was going to end. Nothing came of it. At last the boy began to have secret doubts about the pastor's reliability, but it was a long time before he freed himself of the habit of watching the sky for signs of the coming of the great storm.

Later, Halvor came to be very fond of Pastor Brandt. The very next spring the minister, who was making another tour through those parts, walked past the house and saw Halvor up a tree, investigating a bird's nest.

"My boy, can you tell me if there is a path through the woods to Klemmetsrud's?"

"A path? What's that?"

"Why, a way or a road."

"Oh yes, I'll show you." And he slid down from the tree and accompanied the minister through the woods.

"Can you read Norwegian?" asked Pastor Brandt as they walked along.

"No, but I can read English," said Halvor, who had learned it at school.

When they parted, the minister took a Norwegian A-B-C book from his pocket and gave it to Halvor. The next day he sent him, by a neighbor's daughter who was in the confirmation class, a *Catechism* and an *Explanation* and a *Bible History*, all in Norwegian. The boy grew to love these books; he at once set to work to learn to read Norwegian as if his life depended on it.

As he could speak Norwegian of a kind—that is, the Telemark dialect—and could read English, he made such rapid progress that in no time he had mastered the books. One evening while Anne sat milking, Halvor entertained her by rattling off something he had learned by heart. Suddenly the *Catechism* slipped from his hand and right down into the big trough filled with water for the cattle. The blue binding on the covers loosened and curled up. Halvor cried. He begged Anne not to tell Pastor Brandt how badly he had treated the beautiful book.

The Civil War touches Springville

On the Fourth of July, 1863, news began to spread throughout the land that Union troops under General Meade had won a great victory in the bloody battle of Gettysburg; and at the same time came the tidings from the South that Grant had taken Vicksburg. The government needed men to take the places of the fallen. A huge army was to be raised in order finally to give the brave and desperate rebels a mortal blow and bring an end to the dreadful war.

These events of world history became a part of little Halvor's life, too. For now his father refused to stay home longer. He had to take a hand in the bloody game. He came home from town one night accompanied by an elderly man, a newcomer. After they had eaten their evening porridge in silence, Soren said calmly and firmly: "Well, Anne, I have now decided what I am going to do. This man, Amund Bø, will stay here and help you run the farm. I, too, am now going to war; my mind is made up and there's no need to talk about it any more. I will not have it said to my shame that I stayed at home."

This settled the matter. Anne had to get his clothes out and put them in order, and in a few days everything was arranged.

Soren said goodbye to Anne in a thick voice and told her she would have to look after the farm as best she could until he came home again. Then he quietly kissed the baby in the cradle and turned to go. At this Anne began to carry on. She had a premonition, she said, that Soren would never come back alive.

"Why, of course, I'll be back," he said. "You'll see that with the help of God I'll be back. Now, please be good to Halvor while I'm gone." And with that he was off.

Halvor had permission to go with his father to Ole Kjeldalen, with whom Soren was to ride to town. At first the boy insisted that he, too, was going to war; as that was impossible, he had to be satisfied with going just that little way. Then came the parting. Soren could hardly utter a word. He took the boy in his arms and forced himself to say: "Now you must be a good boy and mind your mother. And you must not forget your father, but pray to God that he may come back to you." Then he seated himself next to Ole in the wagon and they drove off. Halvor

Then came the parting; Soren left for the war

watched them until they passed the turn in the road; then he threw himself face down and wept as he had never wept before.

Soren proceeded to Green Bay, enlisted, and was sent south at once. He was away from home two years, and during this time poor little Halvor was almost completely neglected. Anne always thought he was only in her way. Small as he was, he was put to work—all day long—with Amund Bø, who thus became practically his only companion. The old fellow hardly ever spoke; he was wise, for he had nothing to say. He was with the boy from morning to night, and would work faithfully without uttering a word except for short answers to Halvor's questions. His one interest was in saving his wages. His only luxury was chewing tobacco; this he would cut into small cubes. winding thread around them to make them last longer. Halvor often asked him about the war, but Amund knew nothing.

Nevertheless, the two became friends of a sort. Halvor looked up to the old man as one who possessed boundless wisdom, if he would only impart it. They slept together in the loft; Amund was careful not to wake the boy when he himself got up early. But sometimes Halvor was already awake, and then he would often ask, "Say, Amund, where do you think Father is now?" It was the one thing he was thinking and dreaming about. What in the world was war for? He had heard that they shot at one another. Who could know but what they had shot and killed his father? At the thought he would weep long and bitterly.

And how hard it was to have to work from morning to night while the other boys in the neighborhood were in school getting ahead of him, who had been at the head of his class! He was so tired that he longed for Sundays, when he might at least rest—or for rainy mornings in summer, when he did not have to get up so early. Then he would lie quietly under the roof, listening to the rain pattering overhead. There is something wonderfully pleasant about that sound. It was his greatest pleasure, except for the few times when Anne was outdoors and he indoors, for then he had a chance to play with his little sister and tell her about Father.

Letters from Soren were few and far between. They told only where he was and that he was well, and enclosed some money.

Only a few men were left in the settlement. Jens Knudson was home, for he was lame, and would not have been accepted as a soldier. Klemmetsrud was afraid he would besmirch his soul in the army by associating with so many wicked people; he had hired a man to go in his place. He believed, too, that he was more useful at home, bolstering the courage of the many wives who were in constant fear of receiving a message that their husbands had fallen. The war was the only subject of conversation. But it was little news they received, so far out in the country. They went about in suspense, worrying themselves almost to death. One day official news came that Knud Hansen, who had gone at the same time as Soren, had been killed in battle. A short time later it was learned that Østen Børthe had shared the same fate. Then Halvor Kjeldalen came back minus one eye and brought the news that his brother Hans was starving in the prison at Andersonville. A little

later Ole Findreng came home sick. After his return he
made the rounds of the neighborhood, drinking and visiting the homes of men who were at war, feeling sure of being treated to something stronger than water. He visited
Anne, too. Of course he could not give any definite answer
to her questions about her husband, but he could sit and
brag and tell the most hair-raising stories of the horrors
of war. He himself had killed at least a thousand rebels.
Little Halvor listened to him with open mouth and looked
upon him as an even greater man than Pastor Brandt.

In the spring of 1865, when there was not too much to
do at home, Halvor was allowed to attend school now and
then. There, one day in April, he learned that the war was
over, and a little later he heard a man who had just come
from town tell the teacher that President Lincoln had been
assassinated. Soldiers began coming home in great numbers; wherever one went, one saw the blue uniform. The
whole town was filled with tales of war. People talked of
nothing but battles, and General Grant, and the assassina-
tion of the President.

Presently Anne began to remark that it was certainly
strange that Soren did not return, now that the war was
over. Then a letter came saying that she might expect him
soon. Halvor longed for him so intensely that he cried
every night because his father had not appeared. Then, one
morning, when he came down from the loft, he saw a soldier's blue uniform on the bench near the table; and in
the bed lay his father, looking just as he always had. Halvor seemed dimly to remember having dreamed that a man
had come up to the loft with a light in his hand and had

68

looked at him and stroked his cheek. Now he rushed to the bed and threw himself upon his father.

"You mustn't wake Father. He's tired," said Anne, who just then came in.

But Soren was already awake. He sat up, took Halvor in his arms, looked at him, and said: "Why, how freckled you are! Hand me my pants, my boy."

Never had Halvor been so happy. He stuck to his father's side like a little dog and hung on his every word.

Soren had not changed; he talked very little about his experiences. He was a little thinner, but straight and strong; and the faithful gray eyes had the same friendly glow, the voice the same ring.

Halvor thought it strange that he should have a father who was so much handsomer and kinder and wiser than other men; but he contented himself with the simple fact that it was true. They were as good friends as ever; and the sun shone brighter, the fields were greener, and the birds sang more sweetly than they had ever done while his father was away.

CHAPTER SEVEN

The congregation gets a church and a pastor

Soren had no reason to complain. Anne had managed the farm very well in his absence and everything was in good condition. He set to work at once. He could not see that he had lost anything by his service to his country.

During the first years after the war, times were very good, as most people know. Everyone had his pockets full of money. The farmers got between two and three dollars for a bushel of wheat, twenty cents a pound for pork, and proportionate prices for other farm products. But at the same time, everything one needed to buy was also dear; so a person was nothing ahead. Many people did not real-

*It was touching to see how proud people were
of their new church*

ize this. They knew only that they now had plenty of money, and they began to live extravagantly. They increased their expenses faster than their incomes. But those who were careful and sensible laid the foundation for substantial fortunes.

Among the Norwegian farmers of Springville great changes occurred within the span of a couple of years. They traded their oxen for horses; and in place of their first rude cabins they built good frame houses, often large and commodious. Woods were cleared and brush burned, roads were improved, and the congregation erected a beautiful church.

Soren Helgeson took the lead in this project. First subscribing a handsome sum himself, he went around soliciting contributions until three thousand dollars had been raised. Then materials were bought, and the church was built by Ole Kjeldalen. In a surprisingly short time it was ready, rising in the center of the churchyard or cemetery on the hill. There was not even a dispute about its location, as the churchyard had already been laid out. Thus the reef upon which so many new congregations have stranded was cleared without mishap.

It was quite touching to see how proud people were of their new church. All had contributed and felt that they had a share in it. And for many of them the day when Pastors Preus and Mikkelsen came and dedicated it was the greatest in their lives. Soren Helgeson made use of the occasion to have a housewarming in his new home, which had been completed simultaneously with the church, and both pastors were his guests for the night. Pastor Preus took particular notice of Halvor. He thought him a bright little fellow, and asked him what he intended to be when he grew up. Halvor did not have much of an idea, but rather thought he wanted to be a carpenter. Then Pastor Preus spoke of the school in Decorah[1] and asked Soren if he would not like to send his son there. Yes—that might

[1] The school was Luther College, founded 1861.

be; but he would have to wait at least until after the boy was confirmed.

The next day there was a business meeting of the congregation in the new church. At last Bethel congregation was to take up the matter of calling an ordained minister to be its resident pastor. There was a large attendance and all greatly favored calling someone. But who should it be? No one in the congregation knew of any available pastor. The older pastors who had visited them would, they feared, be too expensive. It would be best no doubt if Preus would try to find someone for them, preferably a young unmarried man who could get along on a small salary. Jens Knudson thought that if they could just once get a pastor, the government would surely support him or at least buy a farm for him. But when Preus explained that in the United States a pastor had to be supported by voluntary contributions from his own congregation, Jens grew thoughtful. He would pay his share, to be sure, but he wondered what Pastor Harbitz would have said of such an arrangement.

Klemmetsrud, for his part, was not certain that they could afford to hire a minister. And besides, there were already a couple of men in the congregation who had the gift of witnessing for the Lord. Surely these gifts should be made use of. He would agree, however, to join in the calling of an "organized" minister if they could be sure of finding one who was truly converted. For such a man would not ask about the salary, but would work because he felt a call to do so and was impelled by a spirit within. On the whole, Klemmetsrud thought, it was too bad they

74

could never have a congregational meeting without always talking about money. And with a deep sigh he sat down.

Soren Helgeson said that he saw no reason for Klemmetsrud to complain; he had certainly not contributed more than he could afford. If people wanted a minister, they would have to pay him enough so that he could live; and this they were certainly able to do. A tenth part of what was spent in the saloon each year would be enough for a pastor—and even give him a superabundance.

The final outcome was that on Pastor Preus's advice they decided to call Pastor Evensen.[2] He had studied at the German seminary in St. Louis, had been ordained a year or two earlier, and was still young and unmarried. The decision about what salary to offer him took considerable time. As he was to serve two other small congregations in addition to Bethel and each would, of course, contribute a little, Klemmetsrud thought that two hundred dollars a year would be plenty. But after some discussion it was decided that Bethel congregation would promise its pastor four hundred dollars a year in addition to festival offerings at Easter, Pentecost, and Christmas, and incidentals. He was to live at Soren Helgeson's until a parsonage could be built. Since he was said to be engaged, presumably he was thinking of getting married and would need a parsonage. It was said, however, that his betrothed had money, and some of the members thought to themselves that per-

[2] Pastor Evensen is a thin disguise for Reverend Even J. Homme, who was pastor at Winchester, Wisconsin, 1867-75 and later founded at Wittenberg, Wisconsin, an orphan's home, old people's home, printing establishment, academy, normal school, and at least four religious magazines.

haps he would be able to manage even if at some future time they should happen to shave his salary a little.

With this selection of a pastor, our friend Jens was very much pleased, for Pastor Evensen, like himself, was from Valders. And as Jens limped his way home, he told everyone he saw that he knew the new minister's relatives in Norway. They were from the parish of Vang, he said, very fine people, and had come to America about twenty years ago, more or less. He really knew all about the minister, too. "He's the one who wrote the gospel about the Pharisee and the publican. And the first time I read it, I said to my wife Helga, I said, 'Helga, a man from Valders wrote that.'"

Klemmetsrud was less satisfied. He would have preferred that they had called Andrewson, who was more low-church in his leanings, or else some evangelistic pastor who they could be sure had experienced a true conversion.

And his friend Hatlevik-Ole, son of the precentor, thought likewise that they could have made a better choice. Ole was somewhat given to going on sprees, a habit which he freely admitted; but he took comfort in the boast that there was not one single word in the Bible which he could not spell. He was, moreover, particularly fond of the Swedish evangelist Linderot's *Book of Sermons* (in Norwegian), the only book he possessed. Linderot was strict, he said, but Ole would not sell that book for a hundred dollars. He, like Klemmetsrud, had little faith in the "state church" pastors of the Wisconsin Synod, as the Norwegian Synod was also called. "They can take Preus," he said, "and Professor Larsen, and old man Stub, and Ottesen from Kaskeland, and as many more as they care to of the preachers of the Wisconsin Synod, and I'll put Andrewson up against the whole bunch and bet a horse to boot."[3]

But Klemmetsrud and his followers were not numerous in the congregation. It was Aanun Strand who voiced the sentiments of the majority when he said that the most important thing in calling a minister was to get one who stood firmly on "the pure, correct, Lutheran alphabet."

Pastor Evensen accepted the call and arrived almost immediately in Springville with all his earthly possessions. These latter hardly constituted great wealth—only an old trunk of clothes and a box of books. Soren Helgeson met him in town and brought him home with his trunk and his box. Soren's new house stood on a little knoll on the south side of the road. In the main wing, the gable of which faced the road, was the parlor. From it a door led to a bedroom, which was called "the chamber" and was used only for guests. From the chamber, stairs led to the second floor, which had three large bedrooms. In the wing to the west were a kitchen (which also served as a living room) a large family bedroom, and a pantry. In front of this wing was a veranda with fancy wooden grillwork. The old house, which stood farther back from the road, was now used as a granary. Still farther back were the stable and haymow. At one side of the house was a garden with apple trees and long rows of currant and gooseberry bushes.

The largest room upstairs, the one with the view of the road, was made ready for the pastor; there he spent the first days after his arrival, preparing his installation sermon,

[3] Kaskeland is a corruption of Koshkonong, an early populous Norwegian settlement in southeastern Dane County, Wisconsin.

on which so much depended. He knew it would be discussed and picked to pieces; and he struggled hard with it, writing and erasing and rewriting until far into the night.

When Sunday arrived, all the parishioners were out early. They were curious to see the new pastor, since he was the first one they could really call their own. They stood about in the churchyard waiting for him to put in his appearance. Jens Knudson was wondering whether or not he, as one who knew the minister's relatives in Norway, dared push ahead of the others, shake hands with him, and tell him that he had read the gospel of the Pharisee and the publican and knew at once that a man from Valders must have written it.

At last Soren arrived, driving his handsome team and light new buggy. And in the seat beside him sat the pastor, a little self-conscious from knowing he was the cynosure of a couple of hundred curious eyes. At the gate he jumped down from the buggy and they got a better look at him. All agreed that he did not seem particularly distinguished. He was tall and thin, fair-haired and smooth-shaven; and his threadbare, greenish-black clothes did not fit very well. He greeted the people with only a fleeting "Good morning" and, satchel in hand, made his way at once into the sacristy. Everyone streamed into the church and took seats, the men on the right and the women on the left, as had been the custom in Norway. Old Hatlevik was even more dignified than usual on this day when, after having been in consultation with the pastor in the sacristy, he came out directly behind him and proceeded to read the opening prayer. He hemmed and hawed vehemently before he succeeded in uttering the words, "To begin with, we shall sing hymn number five; and I would ask someone in the congregation to start it, for I have such a bad cold."

Later, when the minister was to intone the collect and the epistle, a very awkward situation arose. The precentor stood and coughed and made ready to respond, "And with thy spirit." But the minister did not chant; he simply read the ritual; and so Hatlevik, of course, could not respond as he usually did, either. It was most embarrassing. Jens was ready to sink through the floor. And to think how Pastor Harbitz could chant! But this poor fellow could not sing at all. Many thought it strange that a pastor should have no voice for singing.

When Pastor Evensen entered the pulpit, he was ill at ease. He cast a pleading glance at the congregation. There sat the men, some in their shirt sleeves, turning their chewing tobacco in their cheeks as they stared at him. Many women had tears in their eyes, so moved were they. On the front bench sat a row of them, nursing their babies, while others were trying to stop theirs from crying by making them drink from their bottles. Near the door and up in the gallery the young folks giggled.

After the pastor had spoken awhile, his courage returned. He had a well-modulated voice, quiet and unpretentious. He said he had not come to bring them words of worldly wisdom but the simple Gospel of the Cross. Life, he said, was woefully sad and downright meaningless, if one had nothing more to look forward to than a few years of toil and care and then a death without hope. Only Christianity, he urged, could give life meaning. Then he asked their forbearance. One had no right, he said, to expect a man who had only one or two talents to produce as much as one who had five or ten, only that he should use faithfully those he had. That he would earnestly try to do. He would not try to please everyone but simply strive sincerely to please Him who had taken him into His hire. He wished, he said, to be treated like one of the congregation and to share their joys and sorrows. He did not pretend to be more than a poor beggar at the door of grace —one who had been called to lead a group of other similar beggars, seeking the crumbs of the Bread of Life. Before he had finished, the congregation had come to like him. Jens felt greatly relieved. And once more it was Aanun Strand who succeeded in voicing the general opinion when, standing in the churchyard at the close of the service, he bit off a new chew of tobacco and said, "Hang it, he's a corking good preacher, just the same!"

CHAPTER EIGHT

Ministerial timber

The year that Pastor Evensen and Soren lived under the same roof brought much pleasure and profit to both. Since Soren knew everyone in the congregation, the pastor consulted him constantly and found in him a faithful helper. It could not escape him that Soren was a man who was fully dependable. They became staunch friends, and many a night they sat up late, talking and planning for the welfare of the congregation.

Pastor Evensen had studied many subjects besides theology, and he liked to talk to Soren about secular and church history, for these were the keys to a broader outlook on life. He was particularly familiar with the history of Norway, and Soren now heard for the first time of Harold the Fairhaired, Haakon the Good, Egil Skallagrimson, St. Olaf, and other heroes of Norway's golden age. Many in the congregation resented it that Soren and the minister were so inseparable. Soren was certainly no better than the rest, they thought. Perhaps he fancied he was the only one supporting the minister. Well, they would see about that the next time the minister's salary was to be collected.

Our young friend Halvor enjoyed his association with the minister as much as did his father. The two years after Soren's return from the war were happy ones for the boy. When school was not in session, he had to help with the heavy work on the farm, of course; but it was really only fun. For then he was with his father and they would entertain each other, asking and answering questions about the war. Halvor, at least, never tired of this.

The boy had become unusually clever and handy. He could drive the old horses quite as well as Soren; he felt sure he could handle the young skittish ones his father had just purchased, if he were only permitted to try. Occasionally, in winter, when wheat or pork was to be hauled to town, Halvor had to drive a load in; but he did not find it particularly exciting to sit bumping along hour after hour, freezing and clucking to the horses, with no other company than some dead hogs.

For three months in winter and three in summer Halvor attended school. Occasionally, like other boys, he needed to be punished, either with a few whacks across his hand or, what was much worse, by being made to stay in at recess. For the very gravest offenses, a boy might be compelled to sit with one of the girls. Things never went that far with Halvor; he escaped that disgrace.

But, my, oh, my! what fun it was, all in all, to go to school—especially in summer. Then he could go barefoot —that was so pleasant—and besides, it did not take so long to dress. There were only the blue overalls, a striped shirt, and one suspender. Halvor preferred only one instead of the usual two. One was less bother.

In winter, too, it was fun; for then even big boys attended school, and occasionally there was a chance to see a fight among them—usually over a girl. When rivalry grew too bitter, one would challenge the other to fight it out. Having first made a ring in the snow, the combatants took a position within it and, with thick sheepskin mitts on their fists, battled it out until only one was left in the ring. Halvor enjoyed watching this sport, and occasionally tried it himself against Jimmy Mott or some other Yankee boy who made fun of him because he was Norwegian and had white hair.

For his age, Halvor was farthest advanced of all the boys in school, and his father was proud of him. He had spelled down the school several times. On the last day of the winter term, when many parents were present to hear their children speak pieces and to rejoice over the prizes they received, Soren was really well pleased. For Halvor won not only prizes in reading and arithmetic, but also an extra award for diligence. Even Anne secretly thought it was fine, although she was afraid the boy might develop the big head.

In the midst of all these victories, however, Halvor suffered a crushing blow—one which for a time made him weary of life, and caused him to wonder whether he should leave home and go to a new world somewhere, win a great kingdom, come back and ravage America with fire and sword, and overthrow the Christian religion. He had fallen desperately in love with one of the schoolgirls, a charming little ten-year-old Yankee with large brown eyes, a cute little nose, and long glossy curls. She had never actually given him reason to hope; nevertheless, she had smiled at him a couple of times and it was impossible for him not to love her. A Norwegian girl could never be so beautiful as she.

Halvor thought about her early and late, and his heart was sick with love. He was so naive that he assumed, of course, that she returned his affection. And then one day —it was many years before he could think of it without feeling a piercing pain—she said to him, "I like Jimmy Mott better than I like you." It hurt cruelly. If it had only been some other boy! But Jimmy Mott—a dunce who was way behind Halvor in his studies, and who had red hair and sore eyes. It was humiliating enough to drive one mad. The next time he fought Jimmy, he did not stop until they were both so exhausted that they lay on their backs gasping for breath. For, homely as Jimmy was, he was very tough and strong.

Halvor now became a misogynist. No more would he look at those miserable girls. His heart was unquestionably broken beyond repair, but he would bear his pain in silence. No one should know how he suffered, least of all the faithless Fanny, who actually was capable of loving such a boy as Jimmy Mott. Let her go her own way; some day, too late, she would discover her loss.

Pastor Evensen and Halvor had become great friends. In the pastor's opinion the boy was a bright youngster and very advanced in his studies for a twelve-year old. The pastor and the alert, white-haired boy often took long walks together or sat and talked in the study. Those were Halvor's happiest times. He received instruction in Norwegian and even a little in German, and dipped into history and religion as well. Halvor naturally drank in every word; he firmly believed that no one as kind or as learned as Pastor Evensen had ever lived. How he longed to be like him! "It must be wonderful," he thought, "to be the most important person at all gatherings, and always be seated at the head of the table and treated to the best of everything, and yet not be a bit bashful. And then to be able to stand and talk to so many people every Sunday!" The boy often recalled what Pastor Preus had said about the school in Decorah. He began to think about begging his father to send him there.

When Soren and the pastor sat talking way into the night, Halvor always wanted to listen. No matter what the clock said, he would assure them that he was not at all sleepy, not the least bit. It soon began to be noised about through the community that that boy of Soren Helgesen's would be sent to study for the ministry as soon as he was confirmed. Soren, himself, began to think that maybe it could be done, even though it would not be easy to send the boy away for such a long time.

Halvor, squeezed in the pew, needed desperately to scratch his back

Then something happened, which convinced everyone that Halvor, come what may, ought to enter the ministry. It raised him very high in the estimation of the more serious-minded of the congregation; and they agreed that it would be a sin and a shame if Soren, who was blessed with such a son and could well afford to educate him, did not let him study for this calling.

The incident happened in church on a Sunday when the weather was oppressively hot. Halvor sat between his father and another man, so squeezed in that he suffered torments. It was roasting hot and stuffy, and he needed desperately to scratch his back, but could not manage it, wedged in as he was. The pastor seemed never to get through with his sermon. At last the boy's sufferings became so great that his patience gave out completely. He began to cry; then at last he was allowed to leave.

"What made you cry in church today, Halvor?" asked Knud, son of Helga and Jens, on the way home from church. Helga's indignation was instantly kindled. She, who had received Halvor when he came into the world, had carried him when he was baptized, and who had such a high opinion of both his father's learning and his own— she did not need to be told why Halvor was crying.

"You should be ashamed to ask such a question, Knud," she said. "Do you mean to say that you don't know that Halvor, small as he is, has a better grasp of God's Word than many grownups? You might well be thankful to God, big overgrown lummox that you are, if you knew only half as much about religion as that little fellow!"

Jens was of the same opinion. His respect for Halvor increased tremendously. He thought it was almost uncanny, if not supernatural, that the lad knew so much. "Who knows but what he will some day be a second Pastor Harbitz? Well, who knows?" Jens gazed at him and pictured him already in a clergyman's gown and ruff. The only thing that worried him was the unfortunate circumstance that Halvor's neck was so short it would be nip and tuck whether he could wear a ruff.

Later Helga often talked about this incident. Soon it was rumored everywhere that Soren's Halvor had been so moved by Pastor Evensen's sermon about the destruction of Jerusalem that he sobbed and had to leave the church to keep from fainting. He had understood it all and taken it to heart—he, that twelve-year-old boy—although Klemmetsrud himself, who usually was easily moved to tears, had sat there dry-eyed, failing to grasp the high seriousness of the sermon. Indeed, Klemmetsrud himself could not deny there was something to this and could only express the hope that Halvor might be the means of bringing his parents, too, to think seriously of the welfare of their immortal souls.

In Helga, as a matter of fact, Klemmetsrud always met his match, for she was a staunch defender of Pastor Evensen. Klemmetsrud was inclined to criticize the pastor, but Helga always insisted that the minister was a true "Luthrian," and besides, he was as handy about christening babies as any pastor could be. Against such arguments Klemmetsrud came off second best.

Both Halvor and his parents thought the house very empty when Pastor Evensen, after living with them for a year, married and moved into the new parsonage opposite the church. The parsonage was not far away and they could visit each other often; but it was not the same as their all being under one roof. On the other hand, it was a really festive occasion whenever the pastor and his wife came over to spend the afternoon and evening. The pastor's wife, or "Madam," as she was called, was pale and placid, the most genteel lady Halvor had ever known. She was city-bred, and something about her made the boy look up to her as one come from a different and more elegant world, even though she was not particularly beautiful. Halvor was always happy when he was permitted to go to the parsonage with a pail of berries or some other delicacy. Everything about the place was so attractive. The house was not really so good or so large as his own home; but the furnishings were arranged so differently that to him it was the grandest place in the world. It was so elegant that he unconsciously scraped the mud off his feet before entering. In the living room was a contraption called an organ, the like of which the boy had never seen; and the pastor's wife could sit down and play it in such a way that the music was far beyond anything Halvor had ever imagined.

Often he was allowed to sit in the pastor's study, where he found many interesting books. At home his whole library consisted of his schoolbooks, *Pilgrim's Progress,* and the *Memoirs of Gjest Baardson,* that master thief in Norway whom it seemed no chains or locks could hold. He liked these last-named books, especially *Pilgrim's Progress,* which he considered a thrilling romance. He wondered at the strange names of the characters, such as Faithful, Evangelist, Worldly Wiseman, and the rest. How did they all happen to have names that were not used among people generally?

In the pastor's study he read *A Happy Boy* by Bjørnson and enjoyed it. Still, it was certainly strange for anyone to sit down and write a book about a billy goat and a coffee cake. And that Marit from Heidegaardene! What a goose she was!

A Happy Boy was good, all right; but it was nothing compared to another novel he came across, which he read so avidly that it left him breathless. It was a hair-raising story named *The Settlers on Long Arrow.* It had accounts of bloody battles with Indians, murders, and many other thrilling episodes. Woven into it were touching descriptions of the tender love between the hero, Keefe Dillon, and a beautiful Indian girl. These reminded Halvor most vividly of his own unrequited love for his schoolmate with the cute little nose and the curly hair. He was moved to tears whenever he read the poor Indian maiden's declaration that heaven itself was not worth as much to her as a single hair from Keefe Dillon's head. It described his own feelings exactly. Such is love!

About this time Halvor began to take instructions for confirmation, meeting with the rest of the confirmands at the parsonage each week. And he learned many things. One of the first, which a younger brother of the minister confided to him in all secrecy, was that it was just a fairy tale—that story of having found his baby sister under the root of an oak. It was something of a shock thus to learn that not even his godmother was to be depended upon for truthfulness.

From his books Halvor had memorized much, including some things he did not understand at all. He had long been able to rattle off what "Paul wrote concerning baptism to Titus—3:5." But he had not understood what in the world "Titus" was. Naturally, of course, he understood the numbers "3:5" better. For he was sure that they signified either three dollars and five cents; or three feet, five inches; or five minutes past three. And now he discovered that he had been wrong about this, too.

CHAPTER NINE

Off for Decorah

Halvor was now fourteen years old and had finished all his subjects in the country school. His father had not forgotten the conversation about sending his boy to Luther College. But he had an inner battle before he could make up his mind to let the boy leave home. It was hard—they had been such good companions. But Soren said to himself there was no other way; he would have to stand it. So one evening he went up to the parsonage and asked Pastor Evensen to write to Decorah and send in the boy's application. In a few days the reply came that Halvor Helgeson had been accepted. Thus the matter was settled. It was not until then that Soren mentioned it at home. He knew that Halvor was eager to go and felt that Anne would be glad to have him out of the way. Halvor was young, but he could enter one of the preparatory classes.

So he said: "Anne, will you please put Halvor's clothes in order and pack them? He is going to the school in Decorah."

Anne was afraid they could not afford to spend so much on the boy. Furthermore, she wondered if it might not be a sin for plain folks like them to aspire to such high things as making a pastor of their son. Perhaps no blessing would come of it and they would be safer to keep to their own station in life. Nor could she see that Halvor was too good to stay at home on the farm and work like other boys.

But Soren declared the matter settled; the boy was to be given a chance in school; and Anne had to go ahead and get his things ready. Then Halvor went to town with his father. The clothes that were bought for him were much finer than any he had had before. Anne sewed him a couple of stiff white shirts, and since she made them of liberal enough dimensions for him to grow in, they were so large they nearly sawed his ears off.

On the Sunday in September when he was to leave, he was confirmed all by himself. Of course, everybody came to church to hear that boy of Soren Helgeson's who was so bright that now he was going to study to be a minister. Poor Halvor was so proud of being the most important person in the church that, it must be admitted, he forgot what confirmation really meant.

After the services he had to go around and say goodbye to his friends, for he was to leave the same afternoon. Jens Knudson and Helga went home with the Helgesons for dinner. Jens asked permission to give Halvor five dollars; and Helga presented him with a pair of stockings and a pair of red-striped woolen mittens which she had knit for him—which he was never able to bring himself to wear.

After an extended discussion with the pastor it had been agreed that Halvor was surely able to find his way to Decorah alone, even though he had never been on a train before. He was given precise directions about taking good care of his ticket and not giving it to anyone but the conductor, and not forgetting to change cars at Milton Junction. He was told to keep his eyes open and not to be afraid to ask questions if he should have any difficulties. The boy was confident that he could take care of himself; and others thought so too, for he was not afraid to speak up and was not normally fainthearted.

Now he was actually ready to start. His dreams were about to be realized. In his pocket was a purse with fifty dollars in it. His trunk was packed and was already in the wagon. He had to believe it; there was no mistake about it; he was setting out to see the world.

Presently his father drove up to the door and called out that Halvor would have to hurry if they were to get to town before the train left. At this the boy could hold in no longer. He struggled bravely to keep from crying; but when he had to say goodbye to his little sister, the tears came in spite of him. And now, to their mutual surprise, Anne and he made an astonishing discovery. They realized that they really were fond of each other, even though the boy had been told so often that he was only a bother. It took them so long to say goodbye that at last Soren ran in to say he could wait no longer. A lump rose in his throat when he saw how Anne took the boy's leaving; and he felt a new tenderness for her, as he heard her address Halvor as her own boy.

They got to town so late that fortunately there was barely time for Halvor to board the train before it rumbled away. Soren stood looking after it, seized with a strong impulse to stop it and take the boy off. But when it was out of sight he went to the store and bought a handsome piece of dress goods for Anne because she had been so kind to Halvor. Then he drove home, thinking how empty the house would be thereafter. But, of course, he had Anne and their little girl. He would make them as happy as possible. And in a year Halvor would be home for a visit.

Meanwhile, Halvor was sitting by an open window in the coach, staring at the beautiful changing landscape. Good heavens, what speed! What joy and what great fun it was to be setting out on this wonderful adventure! If only his schoolmates, who had never been away from Springville, could see him now. They would be sick with envy. He was a hero, going out into the wide world alone, clad in a brand-new suit and a white shirt, with a pile of money in his pocket. He was going to study and learn so much that everyone would marvel at him.

It was strange, nevertheless, how little difference there was between his home and the world, now that he was at least a hundred miles from Springville. A hundred miles!

He had to smile at the thought. And there, by the edge of a woods, he saw a house which was almost exactly like his own at home. It seemed to have the very same number of windows—one, two, three, four—but before he could count any farther, the train had roared over a little bridge and was slowing down at a station. From the farm up there on the hill came the whining sound of a threshing machine. He could just make out the men working in a thick cloud of dust and chaff. And the man who was standing just outside the cloud, cracking a long lash over the backs of the twelve horses that patiently plodded around and around, looked so tall and straight and strong that he could easily have been his father. What were they doing at home now, he wondered. It was simply impossible to realize that only a few hours had passed since he left. Then his thoughts turned to Decorah. What would the college look like? Everything would most likely be very serious and solemn there, about as it was at home when his father and mother were going to communion. But he would be obedient and work hard; then, surely, no harm would come to him. Thus he dreamed and dreamed until the train arrived at Milton Junction, where the conductor reminded him that he must get off and wait a couple of hours for a train from Milwaukee which would take him farther on his journey.

A group of boys were standing on the station platform. They were all laughing and talking together and seemed to be extremely happy. They were talking Norwegian. Halvor heard them mention Decorah and Professor Siewers.[1]

[1] Professor Lyder Siewers taught at Luther College 1863-77 and was editor of *Decorah-Posten* 1877-1907.

97

Halvor sidled up to the older college boys
standing on the station platform

They also talked about "cramming," whatever that might be. He sidled up along the station wall, to get as close to them as possible, and listened with open mouth. He gathered that the leaders were boys who had been in Decorah before and were going back there now. And he thought that now there was no question of his getting lost; all he had to do was to follow wherever these boys led and he would be sure to land in Decorah. They certainly knew the way. Moreover, he could tell by looking at them that they were bright fellows and had been out in the world before.

The fact that they used a good many expressions he did not understand showed him that they were educated. He also managed to hear the names of some of them. That short, foursquare fellow with the red hair they called Sjur Weeks; and then there was a light-complexioned young man with a hooked nose and dancing eyes and a straw in his mouth; they called him Hogstul. Then there were Ketil Børthe and Joe Svelland and Smith Thompson; and in the care of Børthe there was a little fellow, white-haired and freckled like Halvor himself, and wearing blue-striped, homemade pants and a coat that was much too large. He, too, was on his way to the school for the first time; but he did not seem the least bit shy. He laughed louder than all the rest. And Halvor heard the fellow they called Børthe tell the others that the little, freckled youngster he had with him was called nothing less than Peder Olson.[2]

Halvor wished very much to get acquainted with this jolly bunch, but was too shy to talk to them. Soon, however, they noticed him standing there, devouring every word they uttered; and one of them asked him if he perhaps was on his way to Decorah. Yes, that he was.

Then he had to tell his name, how old he was, where he came from, and much more. One of them asked him if he knew the gender of the German diminutives *chen* and *lein*.

[2] Additional identification of the students mentioned may be found in Strømme's *Erindringer* (Memoirs) and in *Luther College Through Sixty Years*, Minneapolis, 1922, 205f.

When he told them he did not understand what they were talking about, they said that if he could not answer that, Professor Siewers would be very angry with him. But they laughed so heartily that Halvor knew it was a joke, and soon laughed with them.

The train came and Halvor boarded it with the rest of the boys, finding a seat next to the little fellow they called Peder Olson. There they sat the rest of the day and far into the night, enjoying the jokes and stories of their new friends. They were the finest, kindest, and jolliest boys Halvor had ever seen. And to think that he was to be one of them!

Every so often the train stopped and other boys entered, to be greeted by the laughter and noise of the group already there; and the fun increased with each addition to their number.

"Look, there comes Odven!"

"Well, if it isn't Christian Preus! And there is Mandt, and there, Felland!" More greetings and more questions about anything and everything.

"But who are the boys with you, Christian?"

"Oh, some new boys going to Decorah—they are Fosmark and Benny Bredesen."

"Is he a brother of Adolph, perhaps?"

"Yes, of course. I should think you could see that."

"But who in the world is that kid?" asked the latest arrival, "that one over by the door with the blue-striped pants who jabbers and laughs so loud? He surely can't be going to college, can he?"

"Yes, he certainly is. He came with Børthe, who says he is terrifically smart, even if he is so small."

Thus the chatter continued until midnight, when they reached the town of Prairie du Chien, Wisconsin, where they had to wait until morning to take the ferry across the Mississippi to Iowa and then board the train for Conover. Not one of the boys was so extravagant as to go to a hotel to sleep. They sat in the waiting room of the station or went out for walks; and they sang or talked until morning. Halvor thought the time passed much too fast. It would never have occurred to him to sleep and thus miss any of the fun. He struck up a friendship with Børthe's little protégé. They soon became great chums, and each told the other the story of his life and all about his family tree. Halvor told Peder how strong his father was and how pretty his little sister was, and Peder in return gave an account of his family and relatives. The boys discovered they had finished the same grade in the English or public school, and they formed a friendship which was to last as long as they lived.

In the morning the boys went uptown in a body to see where they could get a simple breakfast at the lowest possible cost. Only two were flush enough to go to a low-priced hotel and eat a real breakfast. The rest bought a few slices of bread and a piece of sausage each; this they carried in their hands, eating unabashed while they stood on the riverbank, waiting for the ferry.

After they had crossed over to McGregor, Iowa, another band of boys joined them; and there were new shouts of welcome and more noise and jokes; toward noon they

reached Conover. Here the boys who had been in Decorah
before got busy at once, hiring livery rigs, haggling with
the drivers, and arranging which ones were to ride together. The railroad to Decorah had not yet been completed. The boys all pitched in to take care of the luggage
as if their lives depended on getting to Decorah as soon
as possible. They hunted up their trunks and helped pile
them onto the wagons, and one load after another was
quickly on its way. Our friend Halvor was in a wagon with
five others. Since each had a trunk and a satchel, they
were badly crowded; but that could not be helped, for the
fare was three dollars and there had to be six in order
to make it half a dollar apiece.

The drive from Conover to Decorah was the most enjoyable part of the trip. It was a beautiful, sunshiny day, and
the road down the valley was good. They sang and shouted;
the driver begged them to talk English so that he could
enjoy the fun, too. Hogstul fell asleep and rolled off his
trunk, but the only damage he suffered was a finger out
of joint and they only laughed at this. The road was down-
hill nearly all the way, and the eight miles were all too
soon behind them. Soon Decorah lay before them in the
bottom of the valley. Some of the boys stood on top of their
trunks, craned their necks, and claimed that through the
trees on the bluff to the left they could see the tower of
Luther College. Then they turned the corner downtown,
and there, on the height to the northwest, stood Luther
College, bidding them welcome. They continued at a brisk
trot over the bridge and up toward the stately building,
before which there were crowds of boys, big and little. And

now all the boys driving up stood on their trunks, waved their hats, and shouted:

Hip, hip, hurrah!
Hip, hip, hurrah!
Hip, hip, hurrah!
Luther, Luther, Luther!

CHAPTER TEN

Luther College

Decorah! Strange that this name should have so pleasant a sound! Originally Decorah was an Indian chief who decorated himself by painting a red stripe down his forehead and to the tip of his nose, who was lazy, and who beat his wife if she neglected to light his pipe or bring in the firewood. And yet this name is very dear to many, for it summons up a picture of a place on which the Creator has lavished many of nature's most beautiful gifts.

The heavens are full of majesty. Fair indeed is the earth. Beautiful are the narrow valleys with their soaring cliffs and noisy waterfalls. Beautiful are the endless shores, ceaselessly washed by the waves. Beautiful is the mighty ocean when it glitters, peaceful and calm, beneath the sun's rays or the pale light of the moon and the twinkling stars, or when it boils and foams as the lightning crashes and thunder roars. Beautiful are the vast treeless plains of the West, where the eye, traversing the same endless monotony in every direction, finds no resting place until earth and sky meet at the horizon, and where one feels so small and insignificant that he involuntarily exclaims with the Psalmist, "Lord, what is man, that thou art mindful of him?"

Yes, the earth is beautiful. Everything is harmoniously conceived and gloriously made. The Creator has done all things so wondrously well that one cannot imagine how His work could be improved. And Decorah is one of the most charming of all His beautiful creations.

The Upper Iowa River winds its way between steep, tree-clad hills, meanders through a fertile alluvial basin until it suddenly meets a steep rock bluff and is compelled to bend to the left, then flows for a mile close in to the bluff until it sees before it a broadening valley and scarcely knows where next to take its course; in its perplexity it turns, now to the left, now to the right, until by sheer chance it finds a passage and once more has the high hills on both sides and no longer must worry where to go.

In this lovely valley lies Decorah. If one stands at the spot where the river leaves the steep bluff, one sees to the east the town with its clean houses and its tall church spires. And toward the northwest is a slope which, decked with scattered houses and trees, advances gently upward until at its highest point it ends abruptly and drops almost straight down toward the river bed.

Upon that highest point, close to the edge of the bluff, stands Luther College. The large, stately main building, facing east, looks out upon a beautiful campus lawn, dotted with oak trees to the north. Half a mile to the southeast, nestling in the valley, lies the city of Decorah.

Such is the picture that flashes upon the inward eye and warms the heart when one sees or hears the name Decorah. It has come to mean a great deal to those who spent the happiest days of their youth there, where their horizons were widened, and where they learned that God is great in all His works and manifestations. It has come to mean a great deal, too, to all people of Norwegian descent, for a focal point of their spiritual and cultural life in this country has been Luther College in Decorah.

It was not of such things, however, that Halvor Helgeson was thinking when, as a young lad, he first came to the city. Sitting on his trunk in the wagon, he stared about him as his fellow travelers were swinging their hats and shouting "Hurrah!"

The wagons stopped in front of the main entrance to the college building, and the boys who had arrived earlier crowded about them. "Hello, Mandt! Hello, Christian! Have you had a good time this summer? How awfully tanned you are!" And the fun, which had been interrupted, was resumed as they tried to run up the fifteen steps to the door in three jumps.

Halvor and Peder Olson, the new boy whom he had met on the trip, helped each other lift their trunks down from the wagon and drag them into the hallway. Then Halvor was in a quandary. What should he do next? The older boys, who knew the ropes, were much too busy to bother about the new ones. Halvor sat down on his trunk, very close to tears. His thoughts retraced the shining railroad tracks all the way back to Springville. The distance was too great for him to think of going home and asking his parents to let him remain with them. So here he sat, not knowing what to do next. In the rooms above there was a deafening uproar. Everyone seemed to be having so much fun that he did not dare interrupt to ask for advice. Even Peder had deserted his trunk and was standing just outside the door in the midst of a group of older boys, laughing and joking quite as if he were one of the veterans of the school.

In the corner to the right of the entrance Halvor saw a door ajar; in the room beyond sat a man at a table, writing. He did not look like a college student. Perhaps it was Professor Larsen himself, thought Halvor, and his knees began to shake at the idea. Just then the man looked up and noticed the boy sitting there in the hallway with a pleading look in his eyes. He rose and came out. It was, indeed, Professor Larsen! He appeared to be of middle age, was straight and strong and of medium height. His hair and beard were black, and he had a high forehead with a large scar running obliquely toward the right eye. On the somewhat aquiline nose reposed spectacles, behind which sparkled a pair of piercing eyes. He wore a black alpaca suit and a gleaming white shirt, and he had a long gold watch chain which circled his neck and ended in his vest pocket. As he entered the hall, he pulled a watch from his pocket and brought it very close to his yes. Halvor sat wishing that he were safely back home in Springville. But when the man spoke to him, he knew at once that he had nothing to fear.

"Why are you sitting here?" asked the man.

Well, Halvor somehow managed to stammer that he did not know where to go. Professor Larsen asked him to come into the office.

"What is your name?"

"Halvor Helgeson."

Professor Larsen turned the leaves of a book in which many names were listed.

"Oh, yes, you are from Springville, from Pastor Evensen's charge, are you not?"

"Ye-es."

"Well, you are to study in study room number 1 and sleep in room number 49."

Since Halvor only stared, as if he wondered what in the world was meant by "sleep in number 49," Professor Larsen took him back out into the hall. Just then a young man came walking past.

"Oh, Moldstad, will you be so kind as to look after this boy and show him where to set up his bed? He is to be in room number 49."

Moldstad was a very kind fellow. He looked after Halvor with fatherly solicitude. He helped him set up his bed, fill his mattress with straw, carry his trunk upstairs, and put his things in order. Then a bell rang, and Moldstad said it meant that supper was ready. He took Halvor down to the big dining hall in the basement, still keeping him under his protection. Here, then, Halvor had a chance to see his new companions in a body. They seated themselves at the long tables, and then a tall young man at the head of one table tapped his plate for silence. The room suddenly became as still as a church while the young man said grace.

"Is that one of the teachers?" Halvor asked the boy next to him.

"No, it is only Teisberg."

"What is Teisberg, then?"

"Oh, he is a Primaner."[1]

"Primaner? What's that?"

"Why, don't you know what that is? A Primaner is a student in *Prima*, or the highest class."

"Oh ———" And Halvor stared at the Primaner. He really did not look much different from the rest. But just think what fathomless learning he must have in that head of his! Halvor was informed that the other students sitting up there at the head table were also Primaners. They were busy eating and laughing and were most jolly. "Well, who wouldn't be jolly," thought Halvor, "if he had got so high up in the world and was in possession of such a fund of learning?"

There was more noise at the table than Halvor had expected. Several very attractive girls went about pouring tea and carrying in great piles of bread, which disappeared

[1] Luther College at this time used Latin names for its classes: *prima* for seniors, *secunda* for juniors, *tertia* for sophomores, and *quarta* for freshmen. In the preparatory department (which was discontinued in 1928) were *quinta* and *sexta*.

*An upper classman
took Halvor
in tow*

with astonishing rapidity. A nice elderly woman, who, they said, was Mrs. Crøger, went around supervising everything; and yet the boys laughed and rapped on their plates for attention and were not the least bit shy.

Halvor bravely ate his bread and butter and drank his tea, all the time thinking how much better the food tasted at home. Presently the room grew quiet again as the same young man returned thanks. The minute he was through, they all dashed up the stairs in such a hurry that the whole building shook.

When Halvor reached the hall above, he noticed two Primaners engaged in conversation. Just then a girl passed by and disappeared into a room at the end of the hall. Halvor slowly sidled up to the two great men to hear a

111

few words of the wisdom which would surely be falling from their lips. All he heard was this, "She is, *profecto*,[2] getting to be a mighty good-looking girl!"

So that was the kind of stuff they were talking about! What a shock! But so far as the opinion they expressed was concerned, Halvor had to agree with them. He soon discovered that most of the older students, and the younger ones, too, for that matter, shared this admiration for "the young ladies." He himself did not fall in love with any of them for the time being. He did not dare.

He spent the evening walking around outside; after a while he began to wonder what could be the matter with him. He felt such a strange weight resting on his chest. Finally he realized that what troubled him was longing for his father and little sister and the year-old colt and his friends at home in Springville. At this point, however, the bell rang again; the boys once more stormed down the steps to the dining hall and Halvor with them. First they sang a hymn, then they sat quietly and reverently while Professor Larsen read a chapter from the Bible and offered an evening prayer.

The youngest boys had to go to bed at once. But it wasn't so easy to find number 49 again. With a trembling voice Halvor ventured to ask an older boy where it was and heard in reply, "Oh, go to Texas!" Almost immediately, however, the impatient young man regretted what he had said and added: "Well, come along and I'll show you. But you must be careful not to oversleep tomorrow or it will go with you as it did with John Huss."

[2] *Profecto* means indeed, verily.

Halvor did not dare ask what had happened to John Huss, and besides he was too tired and sleepy to care. He was no sooner in bed than asleep, and knew no more until he was awakened by a man walking into the room, ringing a bell so large that he could hardly swing it. It was already broad day; Halvor jumped into his clothes and hurried down stairs. Fortunately, he met Peder Olson, with whom he had no reason to feel ill at ease. But that youngster already was as much at home as if he had been born on the place. He had plied everyone with questions about everything and had already found out that the first thing they were supposed to do in the morning was wash. So he had already bought a wash basin, which he offered to share with Halvor; and the two boys went down to the washroom together.

Well, that was now done, and Halvor was ready to go to the breakfast table and morning prayers. For the present, at least, he was safe from the terrible punishment which would have befallen him had he overslept.

An hour after morning prayers and breakfast, everyone gathered in the large room used for a chapel in the north end of the third floor. The president of the college now addressed the boys about their duties; Halvor realized at once that he would have to study hard and conduct himself well to be permitted to remain at the school. He decided to do his best and felt sure that then he would get along all right.

He was sitting far back near the door, where he could view the long rows of boys, all of whom looked as if they knew much more than he did. Up there on the front bench sat the grown-ups whom he had heard called Primaners.

who already, it was said, could speak nearly all the languages of the world. On a row of chairs, along the wall behind the lectern at which the president was standing, sat the other five teachers. Halvor grew dizzy thinking how much they must know who were capable of teaching even the learned Primaners. They all seemed to be of an age—about the same age as his father, thought Halvor. But, of course, they would actually have to be fabulously old to have had time to learn so much.

Now the roll of the old students was called, class by class; then that of the new students whose applications had been accepted. Halvor had barely the courage to say "Present" when the name Halvor Helgeson was called; but when that ordeal was over, he felt a little taller than before. Now he was actually numbered among the students of the college. Once, at Pastor Evensen's parsonage at home, he had seen a directory of the Luther College students, and he reflected that the next time such a list was printed, his name, too, would be included. He could imagine how his father would scan the list until he found his son's name.

Near Halvor sat another young lad who also seemed new at the school. He was so very thin that Halvor reflected he would have no trouble thrashing him if he ever had to do so. Yet in other respects the fellow seemed very much alive. His eyes fairly sparkled with animation and he had an unreasonably long nose. It seemed to Halvor that this boy's name would surely have to be Aasmund—but no, his eyes had deceived him; for when the president called the name Magnus Hermanson, the boy answered "Present" so loud that everyone turned to look at him.

So his name was Hermanson! He was the oddest-looking boy Halvor had ever seen, and he decided to get acquainted with him as soon as possible.

When the great event of roll call was over, the schedule of classes was given out; for the rest of the day the boys had nothing else to do but study this timetable, to be ready for the beginning of classes next day. Halvor got a copy of the timetable for the lowest class, or *Sexta*. He went out to the bluff back of the college building, sat down on a stone, and began in dead earnest to commit the schedule to memory. He had never realized how many hours there were in a week. And there were so many subjects that he could not understand how the boys would find time to eat and play ball and swim and fish and do all the other things he had already heard them talk about. Only on Saturday afternoons and on Sundays were there no classes; and every Sunday they had to go to church, he had been told.

The scenery around him was too beautiful, however, for him to learn his schedule. Moreover, directly below him on the flat he could already see a big crowd of boys getting ready to play baseball. Beyond, by the river, other boys were undressing to go swimming. Halvor was just about to clamber down, too, when the thin boy named Hermanson came and sat down beside him. They looked each other over in silence.

"What makes you so happy?" asked Halvor.

"What makes me so happy? Do I look so happy then?"

"Yes, you surely do."

"Well, why shouldn't I be happy? Here I am in college, where I have a chance to learn so much. You're happy, too, aren't you? Where are you from? What is your name? Is your father rich?" These and many more questions were asked.

Halvor gave his name and said that he was from Springville, that his father was an uncommonly fine man, and that he had a little sister who was the prettiest little girl he had ever seen. And Hermanson, who had already learned that it was not proper to call college boys by their given names, to Halvor's great surprise called him simply Helgeson and proceeded to tell him all about himself. They soon became so intimate that Hermanson in all secrecy confided to Halvor that he expected to finish college in just two or three years, so hard did he intend to study. He could not afford to spend very many years there anyway; and, furthermore, he had decided to become a minister as soon as possible, for he had heard that there were places where ministers were needed but could not be obtained.

"I suppose you intend to be a minister, too, Helgeson?"

"Yes, of course, what else would my father send me here for?"

And thus the boys talked on until it was all settled that they were going to try to get pastorates in adjoining parishes so that they could help each other in their work and could often pay each other visits with their wives and children.

Then they strolled around in fields and forest and enjoyed life until the day was done.

The following day the real work was to start.

CHAPTER ELEVEN

Idyllic days

Halvor was scared when, at nine o'clock next morning, he reported with the other boys to the big classroom, where, as their first subject, they were to study Norwegian. His friend Peder Olson was already there with Jensen's *Reader* and a *Grammar of the Mother Tongue* before him, waiting eagerly for a chance to show how smart he was. He would be only too glad to recite for all the others. Then the teacher came. He was a tall man with a wild bushy beard and small bright eyes. His vest was unbuttoned and his trousers hung so low on his hips that they seemed ready to slip to the floor at any moment. He sat down at his desk, ran his fingers through his hair a few times, rubbed his eyes, and then said:

"One speaks in sentences."

This was the first thing Halvor learned at Luther College. And it stuck. Later he learned many other things, which lay, like driftwood, in such hopeless disorder in his brain that he could never make sense of them all. But one truth always stood out in bold relief, "One speaks in sentences."

He had classes in English, arithmetic, German, Latin, and other subjects. The first few days were enough to drive a boy crazy. But little by little things fell into place and Halvor began to get a footing. He discovered that it was not so bad after all. He soon got so that he could repeat Latin phrases like *mensa rotunda* and *stella remota* without trembling.

But Latin certainly was horribly boring. On that point all the boys were agreed. It wasn't a bit of fun until one day they found in the vocabulary the word *rostrum,* a snout. Then Latin suddenly became interesting—that is to say, to everyone except Hermanson. From that day on he was continually twitted about his big nose by the other boys, who would repeatedly ask him if he knew what the Latin word *rostrum* meant. The result was that he was called nothing but "Rostrum," a name he bore with honor throughout his college career.

Halvor's first year at college ever afterwards seemed to him a vague but beautiful dream. Time simply flew. The natural surroundings were so beautiful, the new friends were so cheerful and kind, it was such fun to play baseball and go swimming and wrestle, and it was such an ever-

Halvor's first class "One speaks in sentences"

lasting struggle to learn the lessons, that there simply was no time to count the days or weeks.

The events of the first year that stood out most clearly later in life were the first holiday, the Christmas tree in the college dining room, the first examinations, and the appearance of the first number of the college paper. During the fall of Halvor's first year at college, publication was begun of a hand-written paper which was called *Svein the Fearless*. Halvor was immensely interested in this under-

taking and saved the first issue for many years. There was
not much to it. It contained only some announcements
that were supposed to be humorous, and a long poem entitled "An Unsuccessful Courtship by Mail." This poem,
Halvor was fully and firmly convinced, was the greatest
of all literary masterpieces. He remembered these moving
lines:

> She broke the seal
> And gave a squeal,
> Turned white as meal,
> Then rosy red
> As jam on bread;
> For the letter said:
> "Beloved Miss,
> My source of bliss,
> I now must tell
> That I am well.
> If I might know
> You, too, are so,
> I should be glad
> And never sad.
> I have today
> Something to say,
> To which give heed.
> It may indeed,
> Bring happiness.
> Can you not guess?
> I pine unknown,
> Oh, hear my moan,
> I love you dearly
> And most sincerely.
> If in your breast
> You find the least
> Affection tender

Your heart surrender.
Be mine, I pray:
And name the day.

It is little wonder that the courtship was not successful.[1]

None of the boys will ever forget his first holiday at Luther College, no matter how many other things he may have to remember.

A few weeks after the opening of school, the talk began to go around that it was time to have a holiday. There was an unwritten law that the students were entitled to one holiday in each month. One was now due. They did not so much need a rest, but it was the season to gather nuts and grapes and other good things for Christmas.

One evening after supper, therefore, a crowd of boys gathered outside along the wall of the building. They agreed unanimously that someone would have to go to Professor Larsen and remind him that it was time for a holiday. The weather promised to be fine; so the holiday ought to be set for the next day. Two of the bravest upper classmen were, therefore, appointed to negotiate with the president. The crowd waited with bated breath for the messengers to return and announce the result. Halvor Helgeson was as anxious as anyone. How he admired the boys who actually had the courage to go to Professor Larsen on such an errand! He was almost worried on their account. But now they were returning, alive and safe, and he breathed easier. It could be seen at once that their mission had been successful, for they waved their hats and tore

[1] The heroine was the beautiful Rosine Preus, daughter of Reverend Herman A. Preus. She later married Reverend Jørgen Norby

121

down the steps to the green in such breathless haste that they could barely gasp: "He said yes!"

Then there was rejoicing. But they were promptly told that they must go to the study rooms and do their lessons as usual. That is, they at least had to pretend to study. For if anything is impossible for a healthy, carefree college boy, it is to study in the evening when he knows the next day is to be a holiday and the weather promises to be fine. That is beyond human power.

Next day the sun rose brighter than it ever had before. There was not a cloud in the heavens. The boys were up early; and when they gathered for morning devotions and the hymn "Now Thank We All Our God" was announced, they joined in with full hearts and willing voices and felt indeed thankful to God, it was so good to be alive.

Halvor Helgeson, Hermanson, Monson, Lars Ueland, and a few others of the younger element decided to celebrate the day in the woods. But first they had to go down to the river and have a swim. Down the steep bluff behind the college they bounded; across the flat they raced; then off went their clothes at a furious rate and headfirst they dived into the river. Whew! It really was pretty cold; but shucks, it wouldn't take long to get warmed up again.

After the swim a dispute arose as to what to do next. Hermanson wanted to fish, but no one else was of the same mind, although they would not have objected to fried fish for supper. Monson had ten cents and was willing to spend it for the common weal; so nothing would do but to go downtown first and buy cookies, which they knew would be greatly appreciated before the day was over. This done, they decided that the first trip should be to Ice Cave, about which they had heard so much.

Half a mile north of the city towers a high bluff; on the face of it, about halfway up, there is a cave. Because there is always ice in it, it is called Ice Cave. The boys quickly found the cave and went in. They did not get far, however, before it was dark as pitch. Compelled to feel their way back, they found some stubs of candles left by other explorers. These they lit and by their light were able to crawl to the innermost part of the cave. What made the trip more thrilling was that during part of it they had to crawl on their stomachs, so low were certain passages. What if the walls should cave in and bury them? On all sides were rocks that had evidently loosened and fallen down. It was perhaps best to get out again. How warm the sun shone outside! No wonder it is said that God saw the light and it was good.

Above the cave the bluff is so steep and bare that it is a difficult feat to climb upward. Monson was set on trying it; so the rest had to do the same. A chance to get killed is always worth a try. Without mishap they reached the top, where they had to pause and catch their breath and marvel at the scene that met their eyes. Far below lay the city, and close beside the bluff toward the west was a flour mill driven by water from a spring which bubbled out of the cliff and was conducted to the mill through a long iron pipe. Yonder on the height toward the west lay their dear home, Luther College, towering proudly against the sky. Oh, man alive! What a wonderful world to be living in! From their high vantage point the boys could even plainly see Professors Siewers and Landmark strolling leisurely toward town, and they wondered if these two learned gentlemen were speaking Latin as they walked along together.

But this was not gathering nuts and grapes! And that was the purpose of the holiday. But there was no help for it. The few little cookies which Monson had bought did not go far and they had no other provisions with them. So they had to return to the college for their dinner. Afterwards the younger boys, following the example of the older, wanted to play baseball. Monson was indispensable, for he was an expert player. Small as he was, he could hit a ball so that it cracked like a rifle. And when he ran, one would think that he had been shot from a cannon. No matter where he happened to be when someone hit the ball, he could dash and field it long before anyone else had even seen what direction it had taken. Since the ball game seemed all-important just now, it was decided to let the nutting go until the following Saturday afternoon, when they would make up for lost time. Peder Olson insisted on pitching, claiming that he was a master in that art. But Hermanson batted the first ball straight into his face and he fell down as if dead. That is to say, they thought he was dead, but he soon opened his eyes and began to berate Hermanson for being such a blockhead that he could not bat a ball into the air.

When they tired of playing baseball, they began to amuse themselves by running races and wrestling. A crowd of boys gathered, and Halvor now had a chance to see and admire the heroes of the college about whom he had already heard so many remarkable stories. There was Bentson, who could cover twenty-one feet in a running broad jump and ten feet jumping backward. He was thin and sinewy and did not seem as proud of his exploits as he had every right to be. The boys begged him to show what he could do, but he was heartless and refused. And there was no one who cared to challenge his record. Sagen offered to wrestle with Hogstul or Nordby or anyone else who cared to take him on. He threw Hogstul so that the latter, in falling, skinned his nose on the very spot where it was just beginning to heal since the last time he had fallen and damaged it. But Hogstul did not mind in the least. This spirit was characteristic of the Luther College boys. They mauled each other and only laughed at hurts. They fought each other and were just as good friends afterwards. They were so happy that sometimes their gaiety seemed almost levity. It was not their custom to have long discussions about religion; but everyone who had attended the school for awhile seemed to have absorbed a deep respect for everything honorable and true; and they were closer to heaven then, we think, than they are today, now that their consciences have been scarred in life's hard struggle.

When the holiday was over, the boys ached in every limb. Halvor was so tired that he thought of his bed up in number 49 as his dearest friend. But of course he could not go to bed until nine o'clock at the earliest. How he wished that he were only old enough to smoke and might go to the smoking room, where the noise and merriment could be heard a long ways off. He could not resist going to the door and looking in. There he saw a large number of happy boys who, being over eighteen, were permitted to smoke.

Through the thick cloud which filled the air could be discerned the faint outlines of Thoen and Hans Johnson, who were standing on one of the tables giving a concert. Thoen was singing tenor with an occasional shrill discord, while Johnson with his deep voice sang the bass of "Lift Up Your Eyes, Desponding Freemen." An appreciative audience laughed and applauded and begged them to sing another stanza.

It was hard to get back to work next day, but there was no escaping it. A couple of boys were so bold, however, as to suggest that there really ought to be one holiday more, because those who had gone out and picked grapes and nuts had worked hard and had not actually had a holiday. They felt they had honorably earned a day of rest. Their only consolation, however, was that Saturday, with no afternoon classes, was coming soon and they might then get a little relaxation.

During all these events Halvor had all but forgotten his father and mother and sister. Now he had to take time to write them a letter. He wrote of how many friends he had made, how he had been praised for his good work in Latin, and that his money was all gone; would Father perhaps be kind enough to send him a few dollars? His father, who realized that as Halvor progressed in his education he would naturally need many books, and expensive ones too, sent him the money at once and was glad to do so.

Halvor and his friend Hermanson owned a lamp in partnership; they sat together evenings, studying and helping each other with their lessons. It was really fun after they had got through the first difficulties and understood what was required of them. But it took hard work, too. However, the prospect of another holiday cheered them on, for now the Fourteenth of October was not far away. There was always a celebration on that day, for it was the anniversary of the founding of the college in 1861. The day was spent like any other holiday, except that in the evening there was a program in the dining hall. Several of the teachers and one Primaner made speeches. Ellestad, Nordby, and Førde had practiced some songs, which they presented. Halvor had never imagined that singing could be so beautiful. It was quite different, indeed, from hearing old Hatleviken lead the singing in the church at Springville. And then, when the speeches and music were over in the dining hall, the whole building was illuminated by lighting candles, one in each window. From outside, the whole building seemed to be on fire, all the way to the highest window in the tower.

From Professor Siewer's house, it looked as if a new constellation had appeared in the western heavens, with countless clear stars in uniform arches and rows. And the boys thrilled with admiration and shouted "Hurrah!" feeling that they would proudly and gladly die for Luther College if thereby they could serve her cause.

Winter was coming on. The cold north wind blew across the college campus, sweeping together great piles of oak leaves. Every day the boys went down to the river to see if the ice was strong enough for them to try their skates; they did not have time to wait. It was too cold to play ball, and they had been strictly forbidden to go swimming; otherwise they would surely have done so. At last, one day

127

there was a thin sheet of ice covering the river, and Peder Olson could contain himself no longer. He simply had to see if it would hold him, since he was the smallest of the boys. No thanks! Crack went the ice, splash went the water, and down went Peder. He soon stuck his head up through the hole and called for help. Then, of course, some of the others had to go to his rescue. Surely Professor Larsen would not reprimand them for doing their duty and saving a comrade. They fairly raced to see who would be first to plunge into the water. And what a glorious cold bath they had! Perhaps they might be lucky enough to catch cold and be excused from classes next day. Having finally got Peder Olson ashore, they did not dream of allowing him to walk up the hill to the college. They carried him into the building and up to his bed. Then they all had to change clothes while they talked over the heroic deed they had just performed. What sport it was!

Professor Larsen, however, was not so touched by the occurrence as they had expected. He knew only too well that it was not pure zeal for saving the life of a fellow creature that had driven so many of these youngsters into the water, especially when everyone knew that it was not more than a couple of feet deep. Many of the boys were chagrined to think that Professor Larsen was unable to appreciate heroism when he saw it.

In a few days the ice became strong enough to hold. The boys who had money bought skates; others tried to borrow a pair as often as possible. Ole Arntson was now the hero of the day, for he was the best skater. This was a much greater honor than having the highest marks in class.

CHAPTER TWELVE

Merry Christmas

Hermanson and Helgeson were sitting opposite each other at their table in the study room, working hard to learn the Latin vocabulary for the next day. Hermanson was always diligent, for he was trying to finish his course in half the normal time. But Helgeson was in no such hurry. If he could just finish one year at a time, he would be content. Right now, however, he was studying most industriously. He dared not do otherwise, for he knew it was about time for Professor Larsen to make his tour of inspection of the study rooms, as he did each evening. Professor Larsen had a habit, awkward for the boys, of not

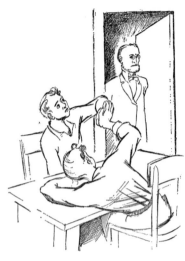

Before anyone knew it,
Professor Larsen
would be
in the room

stamping down the hall so as to give them a chance to
bury themselves in their books; he walked so very quietly
that, before anyone knew it, he was right in the room. He
did not even bang the door as others did. During study
hours, for example, two boys might decide to relax by pulling fingers; and just when they were pulling the hardest,
and one of the other boys had to jump up and grab the
lamp to keep it from overturning—at that very moment,
as they looked up, there would stand Professor Larsen.
The door had not been opened and no one knew when or
how he had entered. It was downright uncanny.

On this particular evening Halvor sat quietly studying,
waiting for Professor Larsen to finish his rounds so that
he might dare bring out from its hiding place behind his

textbooks *Jack Harkaway*, the novel by Bracebridge Heming, which he had bought down at Buck and Raban's bookshop and which was so intensely exciting that it kept him awake nights. At last Professor Larsen came, looked around the room and left, having ascertained that all were working hard. Then, even Hermanson, contrary to his custom, laid his book aside, bent over the table and whispered, "Say, Helgeson, do you realize that it is only a little more than a week until Christmas?"

Yes, of course, Helgeson had thought about it. In fact, the boys talked about it early and late, for at Christmas they had two weeks' vacation. Good heavens! How glorious that would be! Those fortunate enough to live near Decorah were going home, of course; and they had kindly invited some of their friends to go with them. Hermanson was to visit relatives in the country and had asked Helgeson to go with him. Halvor, however, could not decide whether to accept or not, for he was nourishing a secret hope that his father might yet take it into his head to send him money and give him permission to come home for Christmas. Every afternoon when mail was distributed he stood with anxious heart, waiting for his name to be called. One day his turn came. He held in his hand a letter addressed in his father's handwriting. But, alas, it said that although his father and mother would like very much to have him home for Christmas, the trip was too long and expensive; so it would be up to him to have as good a time as possible in Decorah. And to help him make it a merry Christmas his father enclosed a five-dollar bill. From his mother he might soon expect a box containing Christmas cakes, a whey cheese, and some new shirts. With this he would have to try to console himself. He decided to go to the country with Hermanson.

On the last day before vacation no one knew his lesson. All had more important things to think about. The younger boys hated their Løkke's Norwegian grammar and Madvig's Latin grammar and their Cornelius Nepos as bitterly as the older boys hated Cicero, Livy, and Homer. Having classes the last day before vacation was enough to make one desperate. But that was the unreasonable and ridiculous rule of this school in Decorah, and the boys had to make the best of it and fumble their way through classes somehow. On such a day how could anyone with his head full of thoughts of cream mush, spareribs, and Christmas carols give a hang about who was the father of Alcibiades or about any other of the miserable Greeks that Cornelius Nepos was always preaching about?

Time dragged, but evening came at last, and the textbooks were flung aside with contempt. Now they might lie there undisturbed for two whole weeks while their owners were gathering strength to do battle with them again.

A few boys who lived only a few miles from Decorah could not wait; they left the same evening. Hermanson, Helgeson, and some others were to set out on their journey the next day. Their driver had come and it remained only to get an early start in the morning.

The weather next day was so very sharp that Halvor froze his ears before he got downtown; therefore he suddenly made up his mind to remain behind in Decorah.

The severity of the weather, he emphasized, was the only reason for his decision.

To be sure, he had heard other boys tell that there were very good times at the college during the holidays; that the boys who remained had parties in the evenings in the dining hall, to which the professors' daughters and other young ladies came; and that they played "numbers" and other games—thus there were opportunities to get acquainted with these charming creatures. This, however, had nothing to do with his decision. So he said, at least.

Accordingly, he walked back to the college and roamed around the building and was bored to death. Incredible as it may seem, he even reached the point where he picked up one of his despised textbooks just to pass the time away, for he could not possibly spend the whole day writing one letter home. The supper table seemed desolate and empty; less than fifty boys were present.

The next day was Christmas Eve; then things began to take on a holiday air. The boys were allowed to sleep an hour later than usual; and upon coming down for breakfast, they discovered there had been an obvious change for the better in the menu. Instead of only bread and butter and coffee, there was now Christmas raisin bread and sausage and cheese; the coffee had quite a different taste from what it usually had, for they were allowed to pour the milk into it themselves and even take an extra lump of loaf sugar. One might almost imagine that he were home or at a party.

In the evening there was to be a gathering in the dining hall. The boys dressed up in their very best and were all anticipation. They had heard that some kindly disposed people had arranged for each student to receive a little gift of some kind. The gifts could not be elaborate, it is true, for the donors were not affluent.

An hour after supper the party gathered in the dining hall. The older boys were able to laugh and talk and make merry; they had been at such affairs before and were not afraid to look even a professor's daughter in the eye or to talk to her. But with Halvor Helgeson it was a different matter. He was bashful and suffered torments as he sat there. He realized that his clothes did not fit well and that his shoes looked clumsy. Matters did not improve when the presents were given out. For when Halvor's turn came, he received a comb and a little mirror. The only thing he dared say was "Thanks"; but in his heart he was sure that the present was intended as a hint to keep his stiff mop of hair in better order and to look in the glass and see how freckled he was. But how could he help that? His hair simply would not lie flat and freckles could not be scrubbed off. Back home in Springville no one made fun of him on that account; there he was as good as anyone else.

Then Professor Larsen gave a talk on the joy of Christmas. It was so cordial and cheerful and unaffected that Halvor forgot everything else; his heart filled with happiness as he thought of the child that was born in Bethlehem.

Christmas Day passed much like other holy days. There were services in the chapel and the boys felt a quiet spirit of peace and joy afterwards. The day differed from others, however, in one respect; in the middle of the afternoon the boys were invited to the dining hall for coffee.

Halvor Helgeson was beginning to find the vacation tiresome; he wondered how he would get through two long weeks. Perhaps he should have gone with Hermanson after all. Then on December 27, or Third-Day Christmas, as it was called, he heard there was to be a party in the dining hall. That sounded promising.

It was Mrs. Diderikke Brandt, wife of Reverend Nils O. Brandt, who arranged these gatherings. She was always contriving ways to give the college boys pleasure of one kind or another. The parsonage, which was situated on the campus opposite the Main Building, was regarded by all the boys as a second home. Each Sunday Mrs. Brandt invited some of them in for the afternoon; and all of them looked forward with pride and joy to the day when they might receive such an invitation. When it came and they did go over to the parsonage, they always found Mrs. Brandt to be the very soul of hospitality. She found time for everything. She shared the sorrows of the younger boys; she mended their clothes and taught them manners. There was room in her heart not only for her own family but also for all members of their congregation and for the two hundred students, too.

At the Christmas parties in the dining hall she was indispensable. If she was not there, the games fell flat. She knew any number of amusing and harmless ones, and she managed to see that none of the shy young boys were neglected. And she enjoyed it all as if she were one of them.

The first evening our friend Halvor was not sure whether he dared go or not. But he decided to take a look at least. He hid away in a corner and sat gazing at the "young ladies" and a number of young girls who were sitting on the other side of the room, all the time wondering if it would not be better for him to flee.

But now they were beginning to play "Numbers," and before he knew it he had joined the game. Mrs. Brandt took charge of him and gave him courage. The fun of the game consists merely in this: one may get a chance to sit beside a girl whom one likes.

Halvor sat there, both fearing and hoping that someone would call number twenty-two, when he would have to walk clear across the hall in plain sight of everyone and sit down between two of the awe-inspiring girls. He liked them. But he was afraid of them. At last his turn came. His number was called—and, well, if it wasn't one of the professor's daughters who had called his number! She was the very one he had most admired at a distance, and yet it was not for her sake—oh, no—that he had decided not to go to the country. In a trance he walked across the floor in the direction whence the voice came and, strangely enough, managed to find his way. He nearly sat down in her lap, however. It was only a friendly push from a fellow student that prevented this catastrophe and landed him in the chair waiting for him. Now the goal was reached! But what did it profit him? He could not think of a word to say. His cheeks burned; his hair stood on end; and he could not even manage to hide his feet under the chair.

Fate was kind, however, and he escaped his torment, for it was not long before his number was called by a girl with whom he did not feel shy. She was one of the college maids; through her kindness, when he was hungry between meals, he had often received a sandwich down in the kitchen. By reason of her size she went by the name of "Great Eastern" among the boys and was one of the most popular persons on campus.[1] Beside her Halvor was at ease. And yet—strangely enough—if he had only had the courage to talk to those pretty girls, he would gladly have given up a tooth.

Thus the vacation passed, and Halvor began to look forward to the return of the boys and the reopening of school.

When Hermanson returned, Halvor assured him that he had had an awfully good time, but he was not quite sure whether he was stating the truth or not. Hermanson had lived in luxury and glory; now he knuckled down to his studies with his usual zeal and pulled Halvor with him. The midyear examinations were almost upon them. The prospect haunted the boys every waking hour. There was now to be a day of reckoning to determine how much or how little they had retained of what had been taught them. Halvor discovered to his horror that he had forgotten everything. He rummaged around in his cranium desperately, but could find nothing but a few Latin phrases and a few scraps of Norwegian grammar.

[1] The "Great Eastern" was a trans-Atlantic steamship completed in 1858, 680 feet in length and 118 in breadth.

CHAPTER THIRTEEN

Thus pass both winter and spring

"How do you think it will go in the examinations?" asked Hermanson.

"Oh, it can't help but go badly," replied Halvor, "for now all I know is that one speaks in sentences and that in Latin snout is called *rostrum*."

But when the time came, he got along unexpectedly well. He came through the ordeal with honor and was as proud as if he had taken the final examinations in theology and had got the highest mark.

Not long after the examinations Halvor fell into disfavor with the German teacher. There was a little rascal in the class, a boy who never knew his lessons. He and Halvor were good friends and sat at the same desk, and sometimes Halvor could not resist the temptation to help him out by whispering answers when he was stuck.

The class frequently began with the teacher's saying to this boy, "Now, Erickson, you may tell me all you know."

When Erickson remained silent, the teacher would say: "Sit down, Erickson. It appears you know nothing."

Or the teacher might say, "Erickson, tell me the gender of the German diminutives *chen* and *lein*."

"Masculine."

"Nonsense! Bredesen?"

"Feminine!"

"Bosh! Helgeson?"

"Neuter."

"Right, my friend. That is the way the others ought to learn their lessons, too."

Then one day the teacher began, "Erickson, give me the ten masculine nouns ending in *e* that belong to the mixed declension."

"*Buchstabe, Friede, Funke, Gedanke, Glaube, Haufe, Name, Same, Schade, Wille,*" answered Erickson without the slightest hesitation.

The teacher was speechless with astonishment. "So you really know that, do you, Erickson? Or am I only dreaming? This was indeed an unexpected pleasure. From now on, see to it that you turn over a new leaf, Erickson, so we———. What is that you are whispering to Helgeson, Erickson?"

No reply.

"Well, Helgeson, what was it that Erickson whispered to you?"

Halvor did not want to answer, but Erickson nudged him and whispered: "Go ahead. Tell him."

So Halvor came out with it: "He said, 'That fool thinks I know my lesson. But I read the answer out of the book.'"

Whereupon Halvor burst out laughing and the teacher grew angry.

"Erickson, you may come up here. And Helgeson, you may leave the room—because you laughed," he added.

So Halvor had to leave the room. But he was very curious to see what fearful punishment would be meted out to his friend Erickson, so he squatted down outside the door and looked through the keyhole. Unluckily he lost his balance, fell forward, and struck his head against the door so hard that it flew open and he came tumbling head first into the room. He jumped up with a bound and dashed out, slamming the door behind him. But he heard the teacher after him. He ran down the hall and into room number 5, which was empty, shut the door, and put his back against it. But, faced by superior strength, Halvor was soon taken by the collar and asked if he were not ashamed of himself. He turned stubborn and refused absolutely to admit that he had done anything wrong by laughing. Why, the other boys had laughed, too.

There was nothing more to be done about it. But Halvor often had to smart for it. Many a time he came to class, firmly convinced that he had his lesson at the tip of his tongue; yet he would quickly flounder and be told that he ought to be ashamed of his ignorance. He soon became so

He came tumbling headfirst into the room

hardened that he did not take these reproofs too much to heart. Teachers were not so formidable after all. That is to say, with one exception—the President. No boy dared come to his classes without being thoroughly prepared. If they were so busy reading novels or other books that something had to suffer, it was never the subjects which the President taught. If they were ready for him, they felt comparatively safe.

Of course a good many boys conscientiously learned all their lessons. There was, for instance, a big fellow, lately come from Norway, who interested Halvor very much because he wore Norwegian clothes and took everything with a calm that nothing could disturb. He worked hard, like a steady old draft horse straining against the collar, while Hermanson and the other ambitious fellows pulled by fits and starts, like young colts.

This serious and good-natured boy was nicknamed "Full Declaration" after the division of the Formula of Concord which bears that title. Some of the boys had happened to page through the *Book of Concord,* and the result was that the boy from Norway, largest in the class, was named "Full Declaration," while a chunky little fellow, by way of contrast, was christened "Epitome", and a tall, slim fellow had to endure being called "Smalcald Article".[1]

Now there were signs of spring. The air grew hazier and balmier every day. The ice became so soft that skates cut deep into it, making the boys fall headlong and slide on their stomachs right into the water that had gathered along the shore. This watery margin became wider and deeper; some little girls who went out on the ice had to be carried ashore so they would not get wet to their knees. Then the ice, bulging more and more, began to groan, and, with a sharp noise, opened up cracks; and now one could see bottom.

One morning Halvor, who had been out early, came tearing breathlessly in to his companions with the great news that the ice had broken and that huge cakes were floating down the river, which had been transformed into a great onrushing flood and was overflowing all the lowlands. Just the same, the boys had to go to classes as usual that fore-

[1] *The Book of Concord, or the Symbolical Books of the Evangelical Lutheran Church,* contains among other material the Full Declaration, the Epitome, and the Smalcald Articles. *Smal* in Norwegian means "slim."

143

noon. That was cruel. But fortunately it was Saturday, so they had the afternoon off.

Although Saturday dinners were a little better than those on any other day of the week except Sunday, the main dish usually being fish, the boys today paid no attention to that. They could not take time to eat; they had to go and look at the water. Perhaps they might be lucky enough to fall in.

Helgeson, Hermanson, Ueland, Monson, and others of the younger group set off up the river until they reached a place about two miles upstream where the water cut into a steep bank. One huge ice cake after another came floating by. Occasionally one struck the bank and broke into pieces, which continued their journey on the broad expanse of water downstream.

Here was a chance to take a sea voyage. One had only to jump onto one of the ice cakes. True, the boys had a suspicion that it was forbidden pleasure, but what sport it would be, and dangerous, too! Finally the temptation became too great. Hermanson found a long pole with which he vaulted onto an ice cake, just then passing close inshore. He shouted goodbye and sailed out on the wild sea. The others could not resist following him. It would not do to forsake him. What if he should capsize! They had to be ready to fish him out, if need be, at the risk of their own lives. The ice cake which came along at that moment was large enough to hold them all. It bumped into the shore right at their feet. They all jumped on at once and were off to sea. But the ice was wretchedly soft. Pieces kept breaking off here and there and at last the tonnage of their raft was insufficient to carry so many passengers. Peder Olson, who had appointed himself captain, commanded Ueland to jump overboard. But the crew maintained that it was the duty of the captain to sacrifice himself. They were ready to shove him off; before they could do so, the ice cake split down the middle and every man of them slid into the water. Fortunately, all of them could swim and it was not far to land. They were considerably exhausted, however, when they crawled ashore. Still, they all agreed it had been great sport—all but Halvor, whose adventures were not yet over. For he did not crawl up on land but onto another ice cake which was floating nearby and which now started off and carried him to sea again.

In midstream he grounded on a hillock. There he had to sit in his wet clothes with nothing to do but make the best of it. A comfort in misfortune was that a short way off he spied Hermanson, whose ice cake likewise had grounded. The poor fellow, having evidently given up hope of getting his cake afloat, was sitting on his pole, his chin on his knees, his eyes staring into vacancy. He was close enough so that Halvor could see his nose in bold relief against the evening sky.

"Hey, Rostrum, how are you feeling?"

"Oh, I'm all right. How about you? Are you wet?"

"Of course I'm wet, you boob. Do you suppose a fellow can swim around in this water for half an hour without getting wet?"

"What do you think Professor Larsen will say about this trip?" asked Hermanson.

"Oh, I guess he will say that we were good boys and that it will be a great blow to our parents to hear that we drowned in such cold water."

"Pshaw! There's no danger. We shall have to wait until someone comes for us. That's all."

"Oh, it's easy for you to talk. You're dry. But I'm freezing to death. Come over here and pound me to warm me up."

"No thanks. You'd better come over here. You can't get wetter than you are."

This did not sound so foolish to Halvor, so he waded over to his friend. As he pushed up against the edge of the ice cake, however, it began to move. "Take your pole, Rostrum, and help me shove and you'll see we'll get loose. Then we'll pole ourselves to shore."

They tried it and were successful. The water had risen, the ice was almost ready to float off, and only a slight shove was needed. Upon the slope below the college a whole flock of boys stood watching them. Some of them had begun to carry down planks and were going to nail together a raft to rescue their marooned friends. Professor Larsen himself appeared on the scene, just as it was discovered that the boys on the ice cake had succeeded in getting loose and were now steering for shore.

"There stands Professor Larsen," said Halvor. "I only wish he'd come and give me a thrashing to warm me up, I'm freezing so."

Halvor did get his wish in a way. He did get a pummeling so that he was thoroughly warmed up. For as soon as he landed, the boys fell upon him, assuring him that Pro-

146

fessor Larsen had given them orders to see to it that he did not catch cold. They pounded and jostled him and laughed. And he in turn struck back like a hero until he grew so tired that he had to beg off. His only comfort was that the other boys who had been in the water got the same treatment, although they had not had so grand an adventure as he.

In a few days the ice had vanished; the river went back to sleep comfortably in its old bed. A few of the hardiest boys began to say that it was time to go swimming. But they were not yet permitted to do so.

They might fish, however. Hermanson had a remarkable natural gift in this art. When other boys, after repeated patient attempts, had become convinced that there was not a single fish in the river, Hermanson would stand on the bank in the sunshine and haul fish in by the score. This was a great puzzle to Halvor. How in the world could the fish know who held the pole? Or, supposing they did know, why should it give them more pleasure to bite on Hermanson's hook than on any one else's? But such, at any rate, seemed to be the case. The two chums were often out fishing together. At such times, when Halvor could not even get a nibble, he would ask Hermanson to change places with him. But that did no good. As soon as Hermanson moved, the fish followed him. It was pure witchcraft.

One of the serious drawbacks to attending college in Decorah was that the outdoors was so very attractive. It was too hard to study when nature beckoned so enticingly. At least Halvor found it so. While there was ice, he naturally had to make the most of his time practicing skating.

When that was over, it was necessary to make daily trips to the river to see if it was warm enough to go swimming. Up to this time Halvor had never been conscious of the beauty of spring. And as a matter of fact, spring is not so beautiful in other places as it is in Decorah. After only a few warm days, the spacious lawn on which the college stands would be dry, and one could lie on his back under a tree and sun himself and drink life to the full. The Luther College boys seemed to love spring more than did other people. Perhaps it was because on the whole they were happier than other people. Life seemed like a beautiful dream. There were, to be sure, those everlasting lessons to be learned; but this labor made their leisure all the more enjoyable. Perhaps there was some truth in what Professor Larsen was always telling them: that one who does his duty most faithfully is the one who gets most pleasure and benefit out of play.

But if Halvor Helgeson is ever to get through college, he will soon have to get through his first year, that is sure.

To make a long story short—spring arrived with the Easter holidays; then summer came, with Pentecost and the Seventeenth of May and baseball! Before they fairly realized it, the boys had to begin cramming for the final examination. Like a dark, threatening specter, it loomed before them. The great question was, "Will I pass?"

Hermanson felt safe. He even nourished a secret hope that he might be able to skip a year and get into *Quarta*. Halvor, poor fellow, admitted to himself that if the teachers only suspected how very little he knew, all hope would be gone. Possibly he might be able to pull the wool over their

148

eyes. If he did not pass, it would be out of the question to go home. He could never look his father in the eye and admit that he, the smartest boy in Springville, had flunked. He would have to run away and dig gold somewhere in the Rockies.

The examinations, however, were not so bad after all. Halvor discovered to his great surprise that he ranked among the best in the class and that he was slated for *Quinta* the next year. "For I take it for granted that you are coming back next fall," said Professor Larsen.

Of course he was coming back! Where else in all the world could a fellow have such a good time? Why, it was really almost foolish to ask such a question!

CHAPTER FOURTEEN

Home again

The boys were ready to leave for home. But money was mighty scarce. Of course, they had all received some from home which was to have been laid aside for their fare. But there had been so many expenses during the last days. Some had neglected to send their shirts to the laundress in time and so had to buy new shirts for the closing festivities and the trip. And they had to get new hats and pay for windowpanes they had broken. When the time came, several did not have enough money to buy their railroad tickets. The few who had a little more than enough suddenly found themselves very popular.

"Say, Felland, can you lend me half a dollar? My ticket costs eleven dollars and I've got only ten and a half. Help me out and I'll pay you back in the fall."

Yes, of course, those who had money were generous. But no matter how they figured, there was not enough to go around. They were, however, resourceful fellows. A group of ten bound for Madison figured out that by pooling resources they had enough to get as far as Black Earth and still have fifteen cents left. So they decided to buy tickets to Black Earth and walk the rest of the way. The fifteen cents, if wisely invested, would supply enough food on their peregrination to keep them from dying of starvation.

They did not have to go by team to Conover this time, for the railroad to Decorah had been completed.

Great was the commotion at the Decorah station before they managed to buy tickets, but all went well; their purchase was accomplished without mishap. The boys took complete possession of the train. The conductor was a mere zero. He had lost every vestige of authority and merely did his best under the circumstances to see that no one fell off and was killed.

In Conover there was a short wait. At this point they had to separate—some going north and others east. With their coming the sleepy little town woke up. People rubbed their eyes and sauntered to the station to see what was going on. The boys welcomed them enthusiastically, declaimed Latin to them, and offered to bet any amount that Hogstul could lick anyone in all Conover. Then came the train, and away went Halvor and the many others who were bound for various places in Wisconsin and Illinois.

The number of boys dwindled and dwindled; after Halvor had changed trains in Milton Junction, he was alone. At that moment he was thinking not so much about home as about his college friends, although all year he had looked forward to getting back to his father and sister and mother.

Soren stood waiting at the station. For weeks he had been thinking of his boy and rejoicing at the prospect of seeing him again. The train came in with a roar; and the first person to appear in the door was Halvor, tanned, looking very well, and wearing a new straw hat, which his father thought very jaunty.

"Hello, Father!" Halvor could not wait for the train to stop, but jumped off, rushed over to his father, and right away began to tell him what a good time he had had in Decorah, and how much he had learned, and how expert he was at playing baseball, and so on. Soren could not get a word in edgewise. But he was filled with joy and pride; Halvor could see that plainly!

It was not until they were driving home that Halvor remembered to ask about his mother and Jenny. They were well, his father replied, and would be happy to see him again.

As they were getting nearer home, Halvor found it very interesting to look closely at the houses of their neighborhood, which he knew so well. Strange that there had not been greater changes. The old buildings stood there looking exactly as they had before he went away. Well, of course he had not yet been gone quite a year, but it seemed longer. Near a couple of the houses he saw some boys he knew; his father stopped for a moment for him to greet them.

At last, among many fruit trees, the outlines of their own home appeared. It looked very modest after the many big, fine buildings he had become used to. But just the same, how nice it would be to sleep in his old room in the loft!

Mother and Jenny were standing in the doorway, waiting for him. Jenny was shy at first. She had expected Halvor to be a grown man by now, but when she saw that he was still the same boy, she rushed into his arms. Her eyes shone with happiness, and he found her beautiful—much more so than any of the girls he had admired in Decorah.

His mother surprised him by the warmth of her welcome. He went up to her, shook hands quietly, and expressed his joy at being home. The supper table was all set and Halvor was the guest of honor. The usual supper dish was cornmeal mush. But tonight they had cream mush, bread and butter, and coffee.

After Halvor had made a trip to the barn to see the horses, cows, and chickens, he sat all evening telling the family about his experiences. He never grew weary, but rambled on about Professor Larsen, and Professor Siewers, and Hermanson, Ueland, Monson, and all the other boys. There was no lack of subject matter. Jenny wished she could see those boys who were so smart and kind and jolly —especially the fellow whom Halvor called "Rostrum." And Soren was thinking that some time he must arrange to take a trip to Decorah to thank everybody who had been so kind to his boy.

How wonderfully good it felt to go to bed after traveling so far and being up the whole night before! His head on the pillow, Halvor thought of his friends from school.

Halvor had to regale Helga and Jens with all his wonderful experiences

Surely they too must be home, by this time. Now what was the name of that boy, the last one he parted from in—let's see, what was the name of the last small station, anyway? And with that he dropped off. He slept like a log and woke with a start. It was morning. Where was he? Well, of all things! Home in Springville! Of course! And today he had to go and see Jens and Helga Knudson.

Helga knew that Halvor had come home and was expecting him over in the afternoon. She had nagged at poor Jens until, for the sake of peace, he had put on his Sunday clothes. It was not, she said, as if they were expecting an

155

ordinary farm boy. Jens had better remember that Halvor
was now studying for the ministry. So Jens limped about,
busily stuffing this and that out of sight and putting the
house in order. He did not know if he even dared smoke
his old pipe, now that they were to have such a distinguished guest.

When Halvor arrived, it did not take Jens long to discover that the young man had acquired learning. Halvor
had already begun to use "book language," with only an
occasional lapse into the Telemark vernacular. "Isn't it
marvelous what learning will do for a fellow?" Jens asked
himself. "What if Knud, that clumsy boy of ours, could
have gone to college and learned good manners? But that
was not to be thought of for ordinary folks like us. It was
different with Soren Helgeson, who knew how to read and
cipher and speak English."

Helga was not so much in awe of Halvor. "You see, I
know you so well, I do." she explained. "I was the first one
to see you, for it was I who received you when you came
into the world; and I was the one who carried you when
you were baptized and got your name. And I cleaned you
up many a time when you were little, that I did, and
dressed you when you were too small to do it yourself."

Yes, Halvor had known all that before and it was almost
tiresome to be reminded of it. But of course she was being
kind.

He had to regale his admiring audience with all his
wonderful experiences. Jens said, "I suppose now you can
read all kinds of books, even those in very fine print." And

when Halvor said he could, Jens had to move his chair a little to get a better look at him.

Helga, of course, had made cream mush which floated in butter. Halvor had to eat it, and then he had to drink coffee—two big cups of it; it was strong, too.

"You must put more sugar in your coffee, Halvor," said Gunhild.

"No, thanks. It's sweet enough."

"Yes, but you must take more," and she put in three or four spoonfuls of brown sugar. Halvor had to drink it. It nauseated him. But she meant well, and he would not have offended her for anything in the world. However, it was a relief when the visit was over and he could go home and be sick all by himself.

After a few days Halvor had to help with the farm work. He had an advantage now over the previous summer, however; all he needed to do was mention that he was tired, or had a headache, and he could go home and rest. Even his mother realized that one who had studied so hard for a whole year at the "preacher school" could not stand to work all day from morning till night.

Halvor found it a little tiresome sometimes when he met the neighborhood boys, for some of them would tease him by tipping their hats to him and calling him "Pastor" or by trying to use big-sounding words, which, they maintained, was what he did.

As the summer passed, Halvor began to long more and more to get back to Decorah. There was something strange about his feeling. Home was very pleasant. Jenny, his sister, was blithe and sunny all day long and never tired of hearing stories about the college. She liked Hermanson and Monson and Ueland and the rest of the boys, whom she knew so well without having seen them. She was a source of much joy to her brother. He often thought how proud and happy he would be if he only had a chance to show her off to his college mates. They could not help liking her—every last one of them.

His father was kind, as he had always been, and his mother hardly ever complained or scolded. But just the same—it was not like being with the college crowd in Decorah. And so, as Halvor worked on the farm, he counted the days until the first of September, when college would open again. In Springville he now felt rather an outsider. Even between him and his parents there was not quite the same intimacy as before. One day, before he realized it, he got into an argument with his father and was really more positive than was necessary; at last Soren said: "Well, well, my boy—now that you've been at college a whole year, of course you know much more than I. But when you get a few years older, maybe you'll find that you're not so much wiser than your father, after all."

Halvor felt bad to think that he might have hurt his father's feelings; after all, his father was wiser than other men and, besides, was so strong that he could do almost anything; he never lied; and nothing ever frightened him.

There was something else that made it rather hard for Halvor to live at home. His mother now expected him to show an interest in the state of her soul and in the souls of others in the community. She was surprised to find that Halvor could not make himself do so.

One day Klemmetsrud met Halvor on the road, and then and there admonished him to see what he could do by way of converting his father. At Halvor's unenthusiastic response, Klemmetsrud first sighed heavily; later he informed the brethren that there was not much doubt that in Decorah they taught the boys to be freethinkers. One needed only to talk to Halvor to learn that he had no conception of the importance of saving a soul.

When this was repeated to Anne, she was disturbed. She did not dare talk frankly to Halvor, but she often stared at him in a way that made him uneasy. She was wondering if the boy's head really was full of that dreadful atheism. Perhaps it was a sin to let him learn so much. "For I have always told you, Soren," she explained to her husband, "that in my judgment, that is, as far as I can understand it, no blessing comes from ordinary folks trying to get so high up and wanting to be better than others, and now you can talk to Halvor yourself and then you'll hear what strange notions he has, so that I don't know whether he believes in God any more or in the devil or in the Bible or in anything—what has happened to my darning needle again which I just had in my hand as I was sitting here?—was it you who took it, Jenny?—then you'll have to—oh, here it is in my hand—it was good for you, Jenny, that I found it—it would be better if you could learn to leave things alone so that we will know where they are—well, you better talk to Halvor, Soren."

CHAPTER FIFTEEN

A pretty face

Halvor was happy when it was time to go to town with his father to buy new clothes and get ready to return to school.

Strange to say, it seemed harder to say goodbye now than it did the first time. He had not gone far on his journey when it struck him that his stay at home had not brought his father much comfort or joy—Father, who had always been so good to him and had worked like a horse to provide him with money. Halvor even wondered whether he should not turn right around and go home and tell his father how grateful he really was.

Such reflections were soon forgotten, however, for at Milton Junction he met the boys he knew from Decorah. They greeted one another with boisterous enthusiasm. Oh, brother, it was great to see them again!

There is not much to tell about his second trip, except that it was as jolly and as noisy as the first one. There was this difference, however: now Halvor could take part freely in the fun and act as guardian angel to the new boys who were going to Decorah for the first time. Could he not direct them in anything and everything, he who had already been out in the world and had such a wealth of experience? They need have no fear. He would see to it that they reached their destination safely.

In Decorah, Halvor sat on his trunk while being conveyed to the college, just as he had the year before. This time, however, he was so proud and happy that he tried to sing, even though he could not carry a tune. After he had gone to see Professor Larsen, had been assigned a room, and had carried up his trunk and set up his bed, he hurried down to the other boys and began to walk about, sizing up the new students as importantly as if he were sole owner of the whole institution.

He was now in *Quinta*. He realized, to be sure, that it was still a long road up to the highest class. But there was a strange pleasure in being able to look down on those who were one class beneath him. These new boys were very interesting. Some were polished and stylish city youngsters from Chicago; others were clumsy and awkward farm fellows in plain homemade clothes, whose big hands showed that they were used to hard labor on the farm.

162

Soon college work was in full swing. Helgeson and Hermanson were again seated side by side evenings, studying by the light of the same lamp. During this winter Professor Knut Bergh, who had been elected to the state legislature, was absent for a time. All the boys missed him sorely; so much, in fact, that it seemed like a real holiday when he returned and took up his classes again. He was their favorite teacher, always friendly and interesting; the boys looked forward eagerly to his classes. There was not one student who did not love him.

Halvor Helgeson's second year at college passed very much like the first. He did not distinguish himself. He kept fairly abreast of others in his class, was friendly with everyone, took part in all games and sports, and let the rest of the world go by. When the year came to a close, he went home for the summer and found himself still more of an outsider than before.

Then he passed into *Quarta*. Now he realized that he was indeed becoming a man of erudition. For he would soon be taking up Greek, a fact he had mentioned to his parents often during the summer. And they, of course, did not blame him for being proud. Greek! Just think of it!

It certainly was a botheration to learn that language. Halvor lost his courage the minute that Hermanson, who had studied during vacation, told him triumphantly that "to see" in Greek was *horao, opsomai, heoraka, eidon.*

Toward the close of the year Halvor was asked to translate a sentence which, correctly rendered, read, "The Lacedaemonians marched into Attica after the Athenians had forsaken their land." Not having the faintest idea what it all meant, he translated it thus; "The Lacedaemonians used to banish all lazy Athenians to Attica."

The teacher, his eyes boring right through Halvor, said, "You certainly ought to be banished to Attica, too, Helgeson."

Halvor was convinced that he would not pass all his examinations that year. He felt safe in every subject except Greek, in which he knew absolutely nothing. However, when the time came, he was extraordinarily lucky. That year he had begun to shoot up so fast that his pants and coat sleeves were always too short. And his voice was changing. He spoke in a bass voice that every so often would crack and sound so funny that the boys would laugh.

When he was to be examined in Greek, he was first given a sentence so easy that the whole class knew it. They had often talked of it, hoping they would be lucky enough to be asked to translate it in the examination. It consisted merely of the statement, "The Arabs raise many beautiful horses." It was so simple that it was impossible not to get its meaning.

His pants and coat sleeves were always too short

164

Halvor was the lucky fellow. He translated that stuff about the Arabs, feeling that maybe he was not so bad in Greek after all. He was told to continue, but the next few lines he simply was unable to grasp. He began with fear and trembling. Just as he was about at the end of his rope, however, his voice jumped from bass into a shrill, startling sound which no one could understand; before he could get it under control, the teacher said, "Well, perhaps that will do." And the ordeal was over.

When Halvor got home that summer, his mother said: "Why, goodness me, Halvor, how you have grown! You'll soon be as tall as your father."

It was true. Halvor was now almost grown-up. New ideas were surging through his brain; the world had taken on a new aspect. Strange fires coursed through his veins and he felt a burning desire to sin, whatever the consequences might be. He was given to daydreaming and found life unendurably monotonous. He wanted to get out and experience some great adventure.

At home he went about alone much of the time. He could no longer talk freely to his father, as he had once done. Still less could he mingle with other boys his own age in the neighborhood. They really knew next to nothing. Many people thought it strange that Halvor had got no further in his studies in three long years. It would not have been unreasonable to expect him to be able to preach a sermon now. Klemmetsrud, for example, told how the man who married his daughter Liv was able to preach without having been at school one single year. Moreover, he preached in such a way that there was not a dry eye in the audience.

And here was Halvor, who had been studying three years for the ministry and was supposed to be a very smart boy, and yet could not even conduct a prayer meeting. Or did he perhaps lack the will to do so, rather than the ability? Klemmetsrud was inclined to think that the will and the desire were lacking. It pleased him greatly to think how bitterly disappointed Soren must be in that son of his on whom he had spent so much.

If Soren had any such feeling, at least he kept it to himself. He toiled away on the farm, letting Halvor help him when he felt like it and do as he pleased the rest of the time.

In the fall Halvor once more went back to Decorah, with the same uncomfortable feeling of not having given his father much pleasure during his stay at home.

He was now beginning the last half of his six years at the school. He suddenly discovered that it was no great problem to bear up under the weight of his learning. What he knew was really not very much, yet only three years ago he had had the delusion that the boys up in *Tertia* possessed simply fabulous erudition.

Few of the boys who had entered college with him were left. Each year some strayed away, and his class grew smaller and smaller. Those who remained felt drawn together all the closer; there developed among them that deep brotherly affection that one finds only in such a school.

This year there was also a sort of girls' school in Decorah. The pupils, half a score of girls, were daughters of professors or ministers. They had classes in the parsonage on

166

the campus and caused the college boys great sorrow and vexation.

Almost all these young ladies were so pleasant and attractive that they made poor Halvor's heart ache. When this bevy of girls, or *"Comitia Dumriana,"* as they were called, strolled down the road, he could not keep his eyes off them.[1] He was not especially concerned over any one member in particular; but collectively—taken all together —they were irresistible. They caused not only his heart but also his feet to ache. For on their account he began to take pains with his appearance. He forced his big feet into shoes so small that they caused him unspeakable agony. He had to buy clothes oftener than he could afford. What else could he do, even if he sank so far in debt downtown that he did not know where to turn when it came to paying his bills? And what did it all avail him? Not a single one of the silly fair would look at him anyway. When, now and then, he had a chance to talk to one of them, he had no joy of it; he always believed afterwards that he had made a fool of himself. Nevertheless, he continued using hair oil and torturing his feet.

Under these circumstances he found it desperately hard to learn his lessons. Even in class it was next to impossible to pay attention, for, to stop the merciless aching of his feet, he was preoccupied with secret efforts to slip off his shoes without attracting notice. Then, too, there were all kinds of wild dreams. He half decided to run away to the new gold mines in the Black Hills. It would be wonder-

[1] An English equivalent of the Latin appellation would be ''the assembly of the silly fair.''

ful to sleep out there in a tent with a bag of gold dust for a pillow, one revolver in his hand, two more and a bowie knife in the tops of his boots. There he would be able to cut loose; and among the riffraff in the mines and in the gambling dens he would make his name so feared that all business would come to a standstill the moment it was rumored that he had come to town. The teachers fortunately knew nothing of all these frightening plans; they regarded Halvor as a perfectly respectable young man.

He had progressed to where he was a man of prominence at the college. He was captain of a baseball nine, leader in a debating society, president of the group of boys who had to saw wood for an hour every Friday, inspector of one of the bedrooms, and besides all that, he held a number of minor positions of trust.[2] But he felt a certain nostalgia, thinking of how happy he had been the first year, when he was one of the small potatoes and did not have to struggle with Greek, knew nothing about *Comitia Dumriana*, had no debts, and was not so uncontrollably drawn to commit some great sin.

At that time he could safely walk past any store in town. The mention of such firms as Ellsworth and Landers, or Olson and Thompson, had brought no blush to his cheek. He did not owe them a penny. Those were happy days!

Now, on the contrary, he could not go downtown without thinking how painful it would be to meet one of his

[2] In the early days the college rooms were heated by wood-burning stoves. The students, divided into groups, had to saw wood a specified number of hours each week. Halvor had reached the lofty position of being in charge of one group.

creditors. Actually, he had not paid for the suit he was wearing. He could not bring himself to sit down and write his father, to tell him how matters stood; at any rate, he was not going to, except as a last resort. In the meantime he went to classes and took part in all the fun. But his heart was not in it.

One of the students, a son of Pastor Dahlby, and Halvor formed a firm friendship.[3] What the attraction between them was, neither could say. It was not that they were alike, in any event.

Christian Dahlby was a pale, light-complexioned young man who often stayed out of games because he might get hurt. He would not go swimming when it was cold, for fear of catching cold. As for Halvor, it had never occurred to him to worry about his health or to change socks because he happened to get his feet wet. Why in the world should one fuss about such things? But that the minister's son paid attention to such matters made him interesting. Halvor regarded his friend's solicitude for his body as akin to the delicacy of the princess who could feel a pea through twenty feather beds.

The two boys were soon confiding all their secrets to each other. When Pastor Dahlby himself came to Decorah shortly before Christmas, he went with Christian to Halvor's room to meet his son's best friend, as he put it, and to invite him to spend Christmas at his home. The parsonage was a short distance from Decorah.

[3] This was Otto C. O. Hjort, son of Reverend O. J. Hjort, pastor of East and West Paint Creek churches, Waterville, Iowa, 1862-79. The original post office was at Dalby, Iowa.

Such an honor Halvor could not decline. He accepted with thanks.

In Pastor Dahlby's congregation were many well-to-do farmers who sent their sons to Luther College. Each of these boys usually invited one or more fellow students to go home with him for Christmas, and many were the loads of college students that drove off to the Halling settlement at Paint Creek on the day before Christmas Eve. Conveyances drawn by large, well-groomed horses in shiny harnesses with sleigh bells had come for them. The pastor's horses were the best; and the pastor's chore boy, who was the driver, assured Christian and Halvor that he would give them such a ride that none of the farmers' horses would be able to keep up without danger of becoming wind-broken.

Heigh, ho, how merrily they trotted along, sometimes in the shelter of woods and then over bare hills where the wind had swept away the snow! In these places the runners of the sleigh, scraping against small stones, grated so horribly that the sound went to the very marrow of their bones. It was exceedingly cold; the boys stamped their feet on the bottom of the sleigh and pounded each other on the back to keep their blood circulating. In the little village of Waukon, halfway between Decorah and their destination, they stopped to rest the horses and eat and thaw out the tips of their noses. It felt too good for words to get inside next to the stove. It was fun to show off how learned they were by talking German to the fat old brewer from whom they bought lunch. He listened to it all without cracking a smile; and he set the boys a bad example by drinking twenty glasses of beer while they gazed open-eyed.

After an hour's wait they started off again. Now the pastor's chore boy intended to make good his boast that he would drive so fast that the ordinary farm horses would be left far behind. But the farmers had no intention of standing for anything of the kind. They were determined to keep up, even if their horses dropped in their tracks. Moreover they had this advantage over the minister: they could afford to buy new horses if theirs became wind-broken. How they raced! Finally the pastor's chore boy had to give up his crafty scheme.

Later in the afternoon they began saying goodbye to other members of the party at every crossroad. Presently, when they arrived at the top of a big hill, Christian pointed straight ahead to a big stone church and said that the parsonage lay just a little to the side of it, among the oak trees. And then it came into view—a long white-painted frame house, cozily sheltered by great trees.

Halvor felt ill at ease, now that he was to enter a home unfamiliar to him. But this was certainly not the time to think of turning back to Decorah. So in he had to go, willy-nilly, and in no time he felt at home. He had never met such friendly people. The pastor was a handsome, rather stocky man with a closely clipped brown beard and a skullcap on his head. He welcomed Halvor with a sonorous bass voice and a hearty handshake. Mrs. Dahlby was so gracious that Halvor immediately felt like calling her "Mother." And then the daughters, of whom there were quite a few! One of them Halvor knew, in a way, from

Decorah, because she belonged to the *Comitia Dumriana*, but he had never dared to speak to her.[4]

The visit to this parsonage was the beginning of a new epoch in Halvor's life. It was his first contact with family life in a Christian home of cultured people. He had always considered his own home a good one, but compared with this one, it fell far short. Life at the college was jolly and breezy enough, but the boys could hardly be called polite or polished. With them the main thing was to be able to give as good as they got. Halvor was not acquainted with a single family in Decorah. The only social life he had known there, he had encountered at Brandt's, for afternoon coffee on a Sunday.

In this house, all was serenity. At first it seemed almost queer to him that they should all be so polite to each other. Even in ordinary daily life the pastor was as gallant to his wife and daughters as if they were guests in the house. This atmosphere was new to Halvor, but it appealed to him strongly and left a lasting impression. When the family gathered for prayers mornings and evenings and Pastor Dahlby read a chapter of the Bible in his rich bass voice, Halvor felt that he had discovered the wellspring of the love and happiness with which the home abounded.

He had always known that the Bible was a book one ought to read and from which one gathered wisdom; this had been impressed upon him at home and at school. But up to now he had not known that it contained so much that could make life more beautiful, day by day. He had heard

[4] The girl was Louisa Hjort, later wife of Reverend C. K. Preus, the second president of Luther College.

that this book could bring comfort to those in distress but not that it could bring sunshine into the home. Pastor Dahlby now taught him this.

On Christmas Eve there was a tree in the living room. Everyone received gifts. All expressed their thanks and seemed to vie in giving each other pleasure. The tree was not to be taken down until a few evenings later, between Christmas and New Year's, when the young people of the congregation were invited to a party.

At church on Christmas Day Halvor met his college friends who were vacationing in the neighborhood. They all told him what a good time they were having and how pleasant it was to be in the country. In Decorah they were mere schoolboys; here they were students and were looked up to with respect.

Halvor had heard that Pastor Dahlby was not considered an especially gifted preacher, but he could not understand how anyone could say such a thing. Never, he thought, had he listened to such a good sermon as the one he heard this Christmas Day. Even the Christmas offering was a dignified ceremony. In great solemnity the oldest and richest men of the congregation, stooping a little, went up first and, bowing formally, laid their gifts upon the altar. Many who had forgotten to do so earlier went directly from the altar to the women's side of the church, giving their wives money so that they too might take part in the offering when their turn came.

All the Decorah boys were invited to the parsonage to dinner; they envied Halvor, who was privileged to stay there two whole weeks, while they had to leave the same evening, with only the prospect of returning for the Christmas party. For this party Halvor dressed up as meticulously as he possibly could with the few articles his little satchel contained. Christian had told him confidentially that he would get a chance to see the prettiest girl in the state of Iowa. She had a pretty name, too—Nora.[5]

When the young people were all assembled, Halvor felt a nudge in his side and Christian whispered, "There she is, over there in the corner, the one with the long braids."

Yes, she was good-looking, no mistake about that, small and vivacious, with dark brown hair. There was something remarkable about her eyes; Halvor could not tell what color they were, but they seemed to brighten up the whole room. He could not imagine what had come over him. He could not stop looking at her. She bewitched him completely, even before he had spoken a word to her. A little while later, when she came over with one of the daughters of the house to meet him, he lost what little wit he had left. She, of course, was perfectly at ease. Apparently she did not realize what an honor it was to be introduced to Halvor Helgeson, who was said to be one of the brightest lights at the college. Somehow there was something so unsullied about her that Halvor hardly dared take the hand she offered him when she said good night.

When all the guests had left and Christian and Halvor were alone in their bedroom, Christian said, "Well, boy, wasn't she mighty good-looking?"

[5] Nora was actually Laura Marie Ericksen, second oldest of eight daughters of Olaus Ericksen, a builder and contractor who lived in Lansing, Iowa. The fourth eldest daughter, named Nora, became the wife of Reverend N. Førde and the mother of Mrs. O. J. H. Preus.

"Oh, nothing to write home about," said Halvor. But he did, nevertheless, ask a few nonchalant questions as to where she lived, who her parents were, and so forth.

She was a daughter of one of the respected Norwegian families in the neighborhood—very fine people. She was the kind of girl whom all boys worship. "And if you can't see that she is beautiful, I don't think much of your taste," said Christian.

Halvor apparently did not care whether his taste in this particular matter was admired or not. But he thought it was really a shame to call Nora Anderson the prettiest girl in the state of Iowa. Just in the state of Iowa! He was sure that her equal had never lived—if he might say so—in the nineteenth century.

One day before the end of the holidays the Dahlby family was invited to Anderson's for dinner. Halvor made a brave show of preferring not to go—but, of course, he could not very well refuse.

By daylight he found Nora still more charming. No wonder her father and mother seemed contented with life. But Halvor could not understand how Pastor Dahlby could regard her as an ordinary young girl, as he actually seemed to do. And her father! He had the right to embrace her if he wished, but appeared to be too much of a barbarian to be interested.

To be brief, when Christian and Halvor after two happy weeks were driving back to Decorah, Halvor became lost in thought. He was calculating. Easter would come on the last day of March; vacation would begin the Wednesday before, that is, the twenty-seventh. It was now the fifth of January. So, that made two months and twenty-two days. Then he would be going out again to that blessed parsonage which he loved so well. It was a long time to wait. And between him and that time loomed the midyear examination in Greek, in which he was shaky. Added to that was the hard necessity of writing a letter of confession to his father so that he might ask for money to pay his debts.

CHAPTER SIXTEEN

Days of decision

To the other students Halvor admitted that he had had a wonderfully good time during vacation. But he was careful not to say a word about Nora Anderson. If he did, he was sure they would all look her up and try to cut him out.

Halvor pulled himself together and buckled down to work. He would have to study to get through. But it was a hard job. His thoughts were often unmanageable; he could not keep them where they belonged. Just when they were needed most, they would—without his permission—fly out to the pleasant parsonage in the Halling settlement and thence slip over to Anderson's to hover around that Nora girl with the shining eyes and long braids of hair.

In general, however, he fared like the rest of the boys at school—sometimes doing well and sometimes not so well.

He spent the Easter and Pentecost vacations at Christian's home. But he caught only a few fleeting glimpses of Nora Anderson and went back to school more confused than ever.

Thus passed that year and the next. Before Halvor knew it, he found himself at last in the highest class in college.

During the summer he had been home with his parents as usual. In his own community he was, of course, a big man, much bigger than he was at college. His father was proud of him and of his learning; furthermore, Halvor had grown so tall that even Soren had to look up to him. To his old godmother and Jens Knudson, he was a hero. Jens had been shown one of Halvor's Greek books, and his admiration for one who could actually read the likes of that knew no bounds. Why, the letters looked as if they were all upside down; and yet that boy whom Jens had seen grow up and whom Helga had welcomed into the world and carried to the baptismal font could read it just as easily as Pastor Harbitz could read the epistle and gospel.

In Decorah, of course, Halvor was not so important a person. But it gave him a certain sense of pride to reflect that he was now in *Prima* and that he was supposed, therefore, to know a great deal more than the long line of boys in the lower classes.

Many changes had taken place at the college since he had first come there. The main wing had been remodeled and improved. The south wing had been added, giving the building a more imposing appearance. And in the tall tower there was now a bell, bought with funds collected

178

among the students themselves under the leadership of Haatvedt.[1] At the dedication of the bell there had been a great celebration, at which Langeland read a poem he had composed for the occasion. Among other things, this poem declared that the bell would:

> Bring our praise and prayer
> To the throne of love,
> And Haatvedt's name declare
> To the stars above.

Of the teachers of Halvor's first year, only the President and Professors Landmark and Siewers were left. Among the new ones was Professor Jacob D. Jacobsen, who had won the love and admiration of all the boys by his friendliness, helpfulness, and prodigious knowledge. He took a great interest in his students, making each one feel almost as if he were the only one in the class. By his work he infused new life into the college. The students could not help being infected by his enthusiasm for the beautiful, especially for that found so abundantly in English literature. Their whole lives were enriched by their contact with him. His love for what was noble and good was an inspiration.

Well, boys will be boys, even if they happen to be in the highest class at Luther College. And Halvor Helgeson was no exception. Like the others, he cut loose occasionally and played pranks; it is a wonder the patience of the teachers was not exhausted. Yes, what tricks cannot such a group

[1] Haatvedt was Bjørn Edwards, who attended Luther College 1870-75. He became a builder in Chicago and founded the journal *The American Contractor*. He was a great-uncle of Professor C. N. Evanson of Luther College.

of boys hit upon! Occasionally it would enter their heads that it was unreasonable to have to get up at six o'clock in the morning. One day they tried to remedy this by tying up the large bell in the tower, so that the bell ringer was unable to move it. When he tried to get up to the belfry to see what was wrong, he found the door locked and the key gone. This and many other things the teachers had to endure. There was nothing they could do about it. The boys thought it great fun.

In Halvor's last year he again spent Christmas at Pastor Dahlby's. It was remarkable how keen that man was. One day he startled Halvor by asking him if he would not like to go over to Anderson's with him.

"No," said Halvor, "I guess I have nothing particular to go there for."

"What's that?" said the pastor. "You don't think you can make me believe there's no one there you'd like to talk to, do you? Surely you don't think I'm blind?"

And Halvor, who thought his holy shrine was perfectly concealed, became so confused that he did not even protest that the pastor had been mistaken.

Pastor Dahlby was very kind; he offered to write to Halvor's father and tell him how matters stood. "Why, that's impossible!" exclaimed Halvor, "I don't even know how matters stand myself."

Then Halvor began to wonder whether he ought—no, there was no sense in that—he was not even through college yet. It would be ridiculous. That Pastor Dahlby had really understood the whole situation, however, was positively uncanny. Yet it had its advantages, for now the pas-

*I just wanted
to talk to you
seriously
for once*

tor saw to it that Nora was frequently invited to the house
to visit his daughters. So Halvor had every opportunity
that a lover could possibly wish for. He and Nora went
skiing together down the long steep hill behind the parsonage. On Pastor Dahlby's long bobsled they coasted, half
a score of boys and girls at a time, down the road from
the post office corner—way down into the valley—at such
terrific speed that all the girls would simply scream, shut
their eyes tight, and hang on. Halvor always had to take
part in this sport, for he was the only one strong enough
to steer such a big load.

"Come up to the study some time this evening, Halvor,
will you?" said Pastor Dahlby one day.

In the evening Halvor went, his heart beating very fast. What could Pastor Dahlby wish to speak to him about, alone? When he was seated, the pastor offered him a pipe, which Halvor accepted and proceeded to light. He had mastered that art as soon as he had reached eighteen, when the college rules permitted him to smoke.

Then Pastor Dahlby began: "Well, you need not be frightened. There is nothing to be alarmed about. I just wanted to talk to you seriously for once. I believe you are a fine upright young man and I want to help you, if I can. Next year, I take it, you are going to St. Louis to study theology?"[2]

This was something that Halvor had thought about very little. He had been sent to Decorah, it is true, to become a pastor; and he had always taken it for granted that when he finished at Luther College, he would study theology. But lately he had had his doubts. He had read many things that had made the truth of his early religious instruction seem less tenable. Frankly, he did not now know exactly what he did believe. He had never spoken about this to any of his college mates, but to Pastor Dahlby, whom he respected so highly, he felt he could open his heart. He admitted that he had doubts. So many of the things he had been taught he now found hard to believe. Having never gone through a serious spiritual struggle, he had just let things slide, assuring himself with the reflection that what his professors taught him must surely be true.

[2] Beginning in the late 1850's, the Norwegian Synod sent its theological students to Concordia Seminary, St. Louis, Missouri. In 1876 it established its own seminary in Madison, Wisconsin.

"And still you are thinking of becoming a teacher in the church?" said the pastor. "Do you think that is being true to your conscience?"

Halvor replied that he did not know——

"Well, but you *must* know; that is the point. No one has a right to become a pastor unless he knows what he believes."

"Of course, I am not sure that I shall finish college this year," said Halvor. "There is the examination, you know ——"

"That, my dear Halvor, is only subterfuge. I know you will graduate. I have heard that you are a good student. And therefore it would be well for you to think seriously about what you are getting into. I have given some thought to the matter of your future, and I want to offer you a little advice. I cannot, of course, refute all the arguments which men can think up against the truth of the Christian faith. There are many difficult questions which I cannot answer. But I have a remedy with which one can sweep away all doubts; it is so simple and direct that anyone can use it. I learned it from the passage which says 'If any man will do His will, he shall know of the doctrine, whether it be of God, or whether I speak of myself.' If you do not know what you believe, you must not undertake to become a pastor. For the truth is that the most miserable creature on God's green earth is the pastor who is not a pastor with his whole heart. But try my remedy. Don't try to reason away all difficulties, but endeavor to do God's will. Try to do God's will according to the law, and you will recognize the truth that you are lost and condemned to eternal death. Then try to do His will according to the gospel, and you

183

will find that you cannot, indeed, of your own reason or strength believe in God, and that the Word itself not only requires faith but also creates faith. You will experience that this Word is the Word of eternal life. And to all objections of the reason you will be able to say: There are many difficult questions to which I can give no answer, but I can say as did he who was blind from birth, 'One thing I know, that whereas I was blind, now I see.'

"Well, my dear young friend, I am through with my sermon for this time. But to change the subject—what do you think of Nora Anderson? Don't blush. There is nothing to be ashamed of. And you need not answer. I can easily answer for you. If you ever need any help from me, I shall give it gladly, for I am very fond of you both."

It is not too much to say that this was a turning point in Halvor's life. His thinking took on a new seriousness from this hour.

He returned to school and worked hard. Not only his studies, but many other things as well, kept him busy. He was a leader in a college society which was planning a program more pretentious than any that had been given up to this time. He had to practice baseball for the big game with the Decorah town team, which was to take place on the Seventeenth of May, Norway's natal day. At the program to be given on this occasion, moreover, he was to represent the student body as a speaker. This made it necessary for him to brush up on the little—the very little—he knew of Norwegian history, a subject, which, strange to say, was not in the curriculum of the college at that time.

Then, too, he was giving much thought to Pastor Dahlby's advice. But he kept this to himself.

Was it really true—all this about the inspiration of the Bible? Was there really to be a Day of Judgment? Many good people did not believe it. The sages of old, many of whom had conceived and expressed ideas so noble that they made hearts glow with enthusiasm, had lived and died without knowing the Nazarene.

There was no other way. He was always driven back to the same passage, "If any man will do His will, he shall know of the doctrine, whether it be of God, or whether I speak of myself."

He found no solution, probably because he did not seek it earnestly enough. But he was willing to try. He would study theology and decide later whether he had the faith needed by one undertaking to guide others.

At Eastertime, when he was out at Dahlby's again, he grasped every opportunity to sit with the pastor in his study, talking heart to heart. These discussions were a veritable tonic. And the decision to study theology ripened in him day by day.

First, however, he had to make sure of finishing his course at Luther College. He felt he had to watch his step to give no teacher cause for complaint. He did his best to be careful, but ill luck befell him anyway. He and a few other boys had practiced climbing hand over hand along the steel beams under the long bridge across the river, instead of walking across in the ordinary way. And they thought it was fun to entice other boys into trying it, especially those who, they felt sure, would not be able to make it but would fall, kerplunk! into the water. They induced Atlesen to try it. Halfway across, he hung there, begging for help, while Halvor stood on the bridge above, laughing at him. After a couple of unsuccessful attempts to catch hold of the beam with his legs, Atleson, with a bellow of despair, let go and dropped into the icy water. The same thing happened to several others; and, as bad luck would have it, one of them took ill as a result of the freezing bath. From him Professor Larsen learned the details of what had happened, and that Helgeson had invented the sport.

"What is this all about?" asked Professor Larsen. "Don't you understand that one may become ill from falling in when the water is so cold?"

Halvor explained that he had never taken ill climbing about under the bridge.

"No, not when you don't fall in. But you have fooled others into trying it, and one of them is now sick abed." Halvor maintained that no one ever knew whether he would fall into the water until he had tried crossing the river in this novel manner. Professor Larsen would not listen. He made it clear that hereafter, when Halvor wanted to cross the river, he was to walk across the bridge like any other ordinary mortal. Halvor regretted very much getting into this scrape just then, when it was so important to stand well with his teachers. And it was maddening to have so many other things to attend to, when he needed every minute to organize what he had learned for the finals.

CHAPTER SEVENTEEN

Lofty senior

Some time before examinations, however, came the Seventeenth of May, with the address Halvor was to deliver and the baseball game to be played. He and the rest of the team, determined to guard the honor of the college, practiced every day. It would not do to give the Philistines downtown the chance of victory; that would be an unendurable disgrace for the school. Moreover, Halvor simply had to take plenty of time on his speech; the boys had chosen him and they had a right to expect him to do well.

The great day arrived. Halvor was up at dawn, There was beautiful sunshine and the fragrance of spring. The

187

air itself was a tonic. In the forenoon the college boys marched with flags and band music through the city streets, with Halvor at the head as standard-bearer. He could not help contrasting this occasion with his first Seventeenth of May in Decorah, when he and Gerhard Rasmussen, the two smallest boys of the school, had brought up the rear of the procession.

From town up to the campus the boys were followed by a great crowd, afoot and in carriages, which began to gather around a speaker's stand, erected for the occasion among the shady oak trees. Many wagonloads of people, dressed in their best, were arriving from the settlements around Decorah, even from Ridgeway and Calmar and Big Canoe—some from as far as Spring Grove. Halvor was not watching them. He sat behind a tree, alone, reviewing his speech. Up to now he had thought it was really pretty good. Strange how it had deteriorated all of a sudden! Now he realized that it was actually stupid.

But the time had come for him to go forward. The audience had been called to order and asked to sing the Norwegian national anthem. Halvor's speech was to follow. He walked up to the speaker's stand with the chorus which was to lead the singing. On the way he said to his friend Jensen: "Say, John, you are big and strong. If my speech is too beastly stupid, will you be good enough to take me down to the river afterwards and drown me?"

"You bet, my dear crapehanger. You can depend on me. I'll be only too glad to do you that favor, my boy."

But when Halvor got to his feet and with quavering voice began: "Ladies and gentlemen! On this, the birthday

188

of the new Norway, our thoughts naturally turn to the land that lies in the far North————," Jensen interrupted by starting to clap, and everyone else followed his example. It was amazing how this helped. Halvor's courage grew apace, and when he ended with "Hurrah for Henrik Wergeland, who gave us the Seventeenth of May!" and noticed that even Professor Larsen was applauding too, he took his seat, a proud and happy young man.

We have the speech before us now and can testify, on our honor, that it was nothing to brag about; but the student body and the friends of Luther College from Decorah and its environs made an appreciative audience.

Now at last Halvor dared look about him. Well, if there wasn't Nora Anderson, and her parents, too! It was lucky that he had not seen them before. Now, with no apprehensions troubling him, he was able to go over and greet them. He could see that the old folks even felt a bit flattered by this attention from the main speaker of the day. Halvor took them under his wing and saw to it that they got dinner, and he introduced Nora to a select few of his friends —those who, he felt sure, would not make too much of an impression on her. From the others he carefully steered her away.

The ball game in the afternoon nearly ended in disaster. Those young barbarians from town were shamelessly clever and quick. Time and again Halvor Helgeson had to get after his men, warning them to be more alert, lest the game be lost. Nora was as interested a spectator as anyone; once, as Halvor passed near her, she said: "Don't let those fellows win! I don't understand the game very well; but, so long

189

Time and again Halvor had to get after his men

as you are playing, you simply must not lose. I couldn't
stand the disgrace."

Well, Halvor was of the same mind; when he went to bat
with the bases loaded, the students shouted: "Hit her out,
Halvor. Give us a home run!" In sheer desperation, he
swung at a low ball and, to his surprise, smacked it far out
beyond the outfielder; it rolled under the very speakers'
stand that he had graced earlier in the day. Halvor followed the three other runners across the home plate, while
his friends cheered wildly. The victory was won!

The boys surged about him, shouting their joy. Halvor
was a hero. He was modest; but undoubtedly it was he

who had saved the day, and he would not have exchanged places with anyone—not even with Professor Larsen. Especially when Nora came up, beaming, and said she was glad he had done so well; but she also warned him not to let the victory go to his head.

In the evening the boys went down to the river to bathe their aching limbs; afterwards they sat around a big campfire on the shore and talked about the great victory. Later, when they got back to the college, they were hungry as bears. Halvor and some others had to have something to eat, regardless of where they got it. "Great Eastern" was asleep and all lights were out. One of the boys crept through a window in the pantry and handed out a supply of rusks. Next day the housekeeper reported to Professor Larsen that some boys had been thieving; she thought it was the same crowd which had recently committed the dreadful crime of emptying a saltcellar into the sweet soup, thus rendering it more unpalatable than usual.[2]

The year was now nearly over, and the boys were talking about how dreadful it would be to flunk. Now they had to get down to business and study hard! But how could one concentrate on books, when the weather was so beautiful? It was most unreasonable that school should close at this season. Either it ought to end just as spring began, or the college should be moved to where spring and summer did not tempt one so strongly to loll about, sunning oneself on the green. At a meeting in Niffelheim, the smoking room, a motion to this effect, introduced and defended by Halvor

[1] This soup is made of sweetened fruits and juices, spices and water, thickened with sago or tapioca; in Norwegian, *søtsuppe*.

Helgeson, was carried by a large majority.[2] It proposed that a delegation be sent to the meeting of the Synod to advocate that the college be transferred to Tierra del Fuego, or someplace north of Hudson Bay. "For the sake of posterity," cried Halvor, "we must do this, for in such weather no student can, *profecto*, be interested in knowing what *dagesh forte* is."[3] Of course they could not hope to have this change effective in time to benefit them.

"The only thing I'm not afraid of," said Halvor to Hermanson, "is the exam in world history. For Professor Larsen is sure to ask about the dream of Cyrus' mother, and I know that by heart."

Much as Halvor needed to concentrate on his studies, there were always unavoidable interruptions. There was, for instance, an important lawsuit between Jensen and Bakke, to decide who was to pay for a lamp, tipped over and broken one evening when they were wrestling in the study room. Halvor was engaged as counsel for one of the parties. And when his client won, the judge, the lawyer, and all the witnesses for the victorious side went to town to enjoy a treat as guests of the winner. When they got home it was so late that they faced the problem of getting past Crøger, the night watchman, without being discovered. They waited until they saw his lighted lantern at one end of the building, then dashed up the stairs at the opposite end. But the watchman took after them and made the rounds through the bedrooms; he found everyone in bed.

[2] In Norse mythology Niffelheim was a murky region of the nether world.

[3] *Dagesh forte* is a Hebrew symbol.

But Jensen and Helgeson were snoring so loud that he grew suspicious; he gently lifted the coverlet and found them fully dressed, even to their shoes. From this evidence he deduced that they were among the night owls, and so reported the matter, as was his duty.

Two of the boys had been wiser than the rest. They had taken off their coats, vests, and shoes in one of the outhouses; then they walked calmly to their beds under the very nose of Crøger, who, from their appearance, could only surmise that perhaps the butter the evening before had been a little too strong for them and that they were having katzenjammers.

Finally came the last holiday of the year. Halvor fully intended to use it for studying Hebrew. Of course this plan came to naught. Members of Idun, a singing society, decided that they needed a change of diet and that the way to get it was to take a trip into the country to sing and forage. They rented a large wagon with four horses and started out directly after breakfast. Halvor was invited to go along even though he could not sing—because he was well acquainted with the farmers and knew where the boys would receive the most cordial welcome and the most bountiful fare. The trip took them out toward Ossian, around to Calmar and Ridgeway, and then back to Decorah. The boys sang and had a good time and, wherever they stopped, were welcomed and treated to the best in the house. Among those who royally entertained them were the Hegg, Thykesen, Kittelsby, and Holstad families. They got home in the evening, too utterly tired to look at their lessons for the next day.

On that day, however, a heavy weight was lifted from Halvor's mind. Professor Larsen, in the course of reprimanding him for some minor infraction, chanced to say something about "when you go to St. Louis next fall."[4] Halvor heard no more. It was a sure thing, then, that he would get through the finals with a whole skin! Professor Larsen would certainly know, and had mentioned his going to St. Louis quite casually, as if it were settled. The burden of fear that had so worried him vanished. Now he could cease having nightmares about fearful Greek sentences that he could not possibly find any sense in. He was so relieved that, once more, with a good conscience, he was able to sleep right up to when the breakfast bell rang. And when, one night, one of his friends emptied a pitcher of syrup into his trousers, just to see how Halvor would act when he jumped into them in the morning, he did not even get angry. He simply pulled the trousers off again, took the offender gently but firmly by the neck, held him up against the wall, and wiped off the syrup from the seat of the trousers on his hair.

The last weeks of the year were very exciting. During leisure hours groups of boys roamed about among the trees, singing. Whether they could sing or not did not matter. They were not singing for art's sake but out of sheer exuberance. Indoors they played something called "Historical Events." The most important events in world history, with dates, were written on small cards. The players quizzed each other, in turn, on these facts. When a player answered

4 The theological seminary was in St. Louis.

correctly, he put aside one of his cards; whoever got rid of his cards first had won the game.

The words Professor Larsen had dropped about St. Louis gave Halvor courage to write his father, asking him for once to take a week off and come to Decorah for commencement. Soren thought the idea a good one and answered that he would. He felt that he need not deny himself this satisfaction, having worked hard for so many years to give his son an education.

A couple of days before commencement he arrived—just in time to take in a thumping good smoker in Niffelheim, where Halvor acted as master of ceremonies and, as such, made a ringing speech in praise of tobacco. Soren had rather supposed that more important things absorbed the attention of students at the school. But he had to admit that Halvor's speech was amusing. He was, in fact, in great spirits merely at seeing so many happy boys together and observing that his own son, no doubt about it, was one of the best liked of all.

Such gay goings on Soren had never heard in all his life! And the singing! It was all irresistibly entertaining.

There was singing by a chorus called the Bremer Musicians. The only membership requirement was to be so lacking in sense of tone as to have been excluded from the regular music classes of the college. Their selection was the "Bridal Procession in Hardanger." The notes at the close—"Oho, Ohei"—brought forth such a rare assortment of shrill discords that the audience had to cover its ears.

All the boys were attentive to "Helgeson's father," and a number made speeches in his honor. Soren felt that he must make some response, to thank them. He would not, he said, attempt a formal reply; he just wanted to say that meeting and becoming acquainted with Halvor's friends had made him feel twenty years younger, and if they would be willing to accept the price of a couple of boxes of cigars, he would appreciate it.

The next evening the graduates were invited to a supper at Professor Jacobsen's, and of course Halvor's father was included. Here the fun was less unconfined, but no less enjoyable. Much of the conversation was above Soren's head but he rejoiced to think he had a son who understood it all. He got along famously with Professor Jacobsen, and confided to him his pride in Halvor's success.

Soren also met Professor Larsen and heard from the president's own lips that Halvor was a bright young man and had conducted himself well. This gave Soren more satisfaction than anything else; he felt that now he could go home, well repaid for the trip.

The commencement program in the chapel was a very festive occasion, particularly to the young men who were to receive their Bachelor of Arts degrees. It was not, however, a day of unmixed joy. True, they had reached the goal they had been striving toward for six years; but the college had become so very dear to them that the thought of leaving was painful indeed. Halvor Helgeson was tempted to wish he still had another year left. Joyfully he received his diploma from the president's hand and was welcomed into the academic brotherhood; but he felt sad, too, strangely enough, thinking that now his name would no longer appear on the Luther College roster, and that he must say farewell to a place where he had come to know and love every last well-worn stone.

He would have been quite unconsolable had it not been that the classmates he knew best were also going to St. Louis; he would not have to part with them in the immediate future. He and these boys who had grown up together and had drawn closer and closer, as their circle, year by year, had become smaller, seemed more than brothers. For three years more they would be together.

Just the same, they would no longer be in Decorah, and this thought made their hearts ache. If Luther College were ever moved from Decorah, it would no longer be the same school. By the very nature of things it would have to remain right where it was—there on the hill, on the very spot where it was standing.

It was with full hearts that Halvor and the other graduates listened to the president's parting address. He reminded them that more serious times were ahead. He knew, he said, that they loved Luther College and he felt sure they would not bring disgrace upon their Alma Mater. He hoped they would always be a source of satisfaction to him. He wished to stress, in particular, that no greater joy could come to him than to see his children walk in the way of truth.

The time had come for Halvor to say goodbye to his teachers and roommates, and his other friends. He realized that probably he would never again have such happy days as those he had had here.

O, golden days, O life but made
    For pleasure and contentment,

When one is young, a student blade,
    And harbors no resentment
Toward fate for any other blow
Than that one's mustache grows so slow.

When Halvor was not thinking about the sadness of these farewells, he earnestly debated with himself whether he should tell his father about Nora, and take him out to visit Pastor Dahlby. He could not bring himself to do so. Better go back to Springville for the present, and possess his soul in patience.

On the journey home the boys seemed as jolly as ever, but Halvor did not feel quite so lighthearted; at each successive station he said goodbye to friends whom he could not expect to see again for years. At Milton Junction Soren treated the boys who were still together to dinner. After that he and Halvor were alone until they reached home.

"What do you think of Luther College and Decorah, Father?"

"Oh, I'm very glad I made the trip. I wouldn't have missed it for anything. It was worth a trip around the world just to have a little talk with Professor Jacobsen. And all those boys! You know, I've been plodding along at home all these years alone; and those boys, why it was a treat just to look at them. Halvor, I want you to know I'm glad I sent you to Decorah. But now let's talk about something else. Next fall I suppose you're going to St. Louis?"

"Well, I guess you're the one to decide that, Father. For if I go to St. Louis, you'll be the one to furnish the money, you know."

"Yes, of course I do. But is it all settled now that you want to be a minister?"

"Yes, I think so; but I can't be sure of it yet."

All summer Halvor worked hard on the farm. His father reminded him occasionally that he need not go at it so intensely. But Halvor felt he had to keep busy. It was no fun to go around visiting the neighbors. The only ones whom he felt he should see were Jens and Helga Knudson. They had followed his progress at school with as much interest as if he had been their very own.

"For you see," said Helga, "it isn't as if you were a stranger. But you've grown so big and tall, and have so much book learning that I probably shouldn't talk to you like this. Just the same, it's very nice of you to come over and visit us, and now you certainly must stay for supper and I'll see that you get the best coffee I can make; and then I hope you'll be willing to accept these socks I've knit for you; my only wish is that you may have health to wear them out. And Jens here thought he would like to give you a few measly dollars to have with you at the preacher school in St. Lud— what was it now that your father called that place?"

So Jens pulled a bill out of his pocket, mumbling something about the amount being so little that it was a shame to offer it, but perhaps Halvor could use it to buy a minister's ruff.

CHAPTER EIGHTEEN

Theological student at St. Louis

"Now, you must be careful not to get lost down there in Chicago," said Soren Helgeson, as his son was leaving to study theology at the German Concordia Seminary in St. Louis.

To Halvor his advice seemed superfluous. To be sure he had never been in a metropolis; but he had traveled quite a bit and was so well able to look out for himself that he could get along anywhere and everywhere. Besides, it was high time for him to see a little of the world. Therefore, he was starting out a couple of days early, to have a chance to see Chicago on his way to St. Louis.

As he sat in the railroad coach, he hoped to be lucky enough to meet some of his Decorah schoolmates in Chicago.

Toward evening there were evidences that the great city was near. From the window he saw large factories, and long rows of small frame houses scattered here and there over the prairie, and then again open spaces, with white-painted billboards announcing that right there the very finest building lots could be purchased at the lowest possible prices and on the best terms.

At last the train bravely plunged right into the thick cloud of smoke that hid the city from view. A short time later it stopped in the midst of the noise and smell. Halvor followed the other passengers and soon found himself on the street with its deafening noise, dickering with the many cabbies who sought to drive him to a hotel. He managed to fend them off, thinking himself quite a fellow for doing so. But right afterwards he made the painful discovery that he was only a green boy from the country after all. He, who had graduated from college and who thought he knew everything, was made a fool of by just a ragged little bootblack! This bootblack, who had evidently sized him up at a glance, walked up to him and said "Shine, sir?" Naturally, Halvor thought it would not be a bad idea to have his shoes shined before he showed himself in the city. When the job was done, he offered the boy ten cents. The little scamp refused the money scornfully. He was not, he said, an ordinary bootblack, of the kind to be found everywhere on the streets. His price was twenty-five cents. He was so authoritative that Halvor paid what he demanded, only to have a bystander tell him that five cents was the usual price. How that galled him! He did not so much mind losing those few pennies, but it was mortifying to learn how plainly he showed that he was from the country.

Now that he was beginning to spruce up, he might as well get his unruly locks cut, he thought. He soon found an unpretentious place in a basement. When the Negro who was apparently the boss stroked his face and said that he needed a shave as well as a haircut, Halvor could not muster the courage to tell him, even though it was true, that his face was still as smooth as a newly laid egg. He was glad to escape with a whole skin. He found his way to a modest hotel, where he had supper and engaged a room for the night.

This done, he strolled up and down the streets for a time; the bewildering array of shops, stretching for miles and miles in every direction, made his head swim. There were brilliantly lighted saloons, too, glittering with gilt and mirrors, interspersed with tumble-down wooden houses, before which sat ragged and dirty women with half-starved children in their arms. There were also shabby cubicles where sottish women, black and white, stood in the door-ways, soliciting with profanities and obscenities, while others leaned from the windows, their ugly, horrid, painted faces leering at the men passing by.

On the street corner stood a man in a wagon, baking waffles and crying his wares; beside him sat a blind old woman, turning a hand organ with one hand and holding out a tin box for alms with the other. It was all nauseating. Halvor had backbone enough to say "No" when a black-bearded man with a black eye, who smelled strongly of whiskey, sidled up and whispered hoarsely: "Could you spare a quarter, friend? I've been in hospital two months, sick as a dog."

Halvor, finding his way back to the hotel, was lucky to escape being run over by a fire engine drawn by wildly galloping horses. It came tearing down the street, followed by the usual crowd of men and boys, hurrying and scurrying for a chance to feast their eyes on the horrors of a fire.

When he found himself safe again at the hotel, Halvor thought he was entitled to smoke a cigar. It calmed him and helped him think. How in the world did all these people live? Where did all the countless shopkeepers get their business? And those awful women with their bloated painted faces! For shame! What nastiness there was in the world! Halvor felt as if he had besmirched his soul just by looking at them.

Stepping outside the hotel for a breath of air, he was accosted by an exceedingly amiable individual who said that he had taken to Halvor at sight because of his open, honest face. The man offered to take him to a cozy place where they could while away the time in a quiet little game of cards. When Halvor declined, the man became still more affable and assured him that by refusing he had risen still higher in his estimation. Cards, he said, were best avoided. And, finding Halvor to be such an exemplary young man, he had decided to do him a good turn. He had by chance come into possession of a gold watch, which he was going to sell for next to nothing, as he already had one and happened just then to need a little cash. Selling it for twenty dollars would be giving it away, he said. But since he had taken such a fancy to Halvor, he would let him have it for practically nothing—that is, for fifteen dollars.

It hurt Halvor to have to decline the offer. But he really could not afford a new watch; the old silver one his father had given him would have to do.

When it was time to leave for St. Louis the next day, new trials awaited him. He asked about when his train left and from which station, but no one in Chicago would admit that there was such a place as St. Louis. Some people he asked insisted they had never heard of such a town; others admitted that somewhere way off southwest there was said to be a cemetery by that name.

At that time Chicago and St. Louis were of about equal size and therefore bitter rivals. When Halvor finally got to St. Louis, he found that people there, in a similar way, pretended they had only the faintest recollection of hearing a rumor that there was a village said to be called Chicago. But they were not quite sure of it.

In Chicago, however, Halvor at last found a man who was willing to admit there actually was a paltry little dump named St. Louis, and that he could get a train for it at the station nearby on Canal Street.

The journey took him through many attractive small towns surrounded by great cornfields stretching over the plain. The two hundred and fifty miles were covered in nine hours; at dusk the train rumbled over a great bridge, through a tunnel a mile long, and finally stopped in an underground area, from which travelers ascended broad stairs to the ground floor level, rubbed their eyes, and found themselves in the center of the city.

Not until Halvor noted the great size of this city, so little known in Chicago, did he remember that he had not the slightest idea of where to find Concordia Seminary. He had completely overlooked this detail.

Since it was evening, he decided to go to a hotel for the night and start out early the next morning to search for the school. Even then he did not have enough sense to look for it in a directory, but started out on a hit-or-miss hunt.

In the course of the day he found a number of schools but never the right one. Just as he was beginning to lose hope, he ran across a German saloonkeeper in the south part of the city who said that he did not know of any school named Concordia Seminary, but that the big gray brick building down on the corner was the "Saxon College," and in the house behind it lived Professors Guenther and Schaller, and in the one a little farther north, among the trees, lived Professor Walther.[1] Another man who happened by explained that, sure enough, the school was also sometimes called Concordia Seminary.

That problem was solved. Halvor had started only a short way toward the building when he heard, "Well, well, there comes Helgeson, too!" Looking up, he saw Hermanson, Gabrielson, and a number of other old friends on the steps.

[1] The name "Saxon College" was used because the early German Missouri Synod founders came from Saxony.

206

"Good heavens! How good it is to see you after tramping around all day, asking my way in German!"

"But, my dear fellow, why in the world didn't you get full instructions before you started out?"

"Yes, you may well ask. But do you think I had sense enough to do that? If you live long enough, you will eventually discover that I'm nothing more nor less than a blooming idiot."

The seminary appeared fairly spacious. But it had been erected at three different periods by as many architects, each of whom had paid no attention to the work of his predecessors. Clearly, they must have consulted John Barleycorn when they drew their plans. From the main wing one could not get to either of the side wings without going through all the bedrooms, up a few stairs, out onto a veranda, and then into whichever wing one wished to reach.

It was an unwritten law at the seminary that three of the best study rooms be set aside for the Norwegians, of whom there were about twenty in Halvor's day as against five times as many Germans. Before the "practical seminary" had been moved to Springfield, enrollment at the school had been much larger.[2] In that earlier time the Norwegian students were quartered in various other buildings in the neighborhood, most of them in one room, which was called "Hututu."[3]

[2] The term "practical seminary" was used as opposed to the theoretical or philosophical seminary. The latter required a thorough knowledge of the ancient languages.

[3] A possible English equivalent might be, "All hope abandon, ye who enter here."

Halvor was shown up to Professor Walther's study

Halvor found that his friends had reserved a place for him in "Asgard," as they had named the best of the rooms assigned to the Norwegians. It was close to the stairs at the left, in the second story of the main wing. In the room next to Asgard, but slightly more elevated, was "Valhalla." It might as well have been at the far end of town, however, it was so difficult to get to. In the basement of the main wing was the dining room, where Frau Jungkunz, a plump and buxom housekeeper, ruled, making sure that no one ate too much. Directly above the dining room was the auditorium, or Aula, as it was called, where the students held indignation meetings when the meals became altogether too Spartan.

Halvor, after getting comfortably settled in Asgard, went over to announce his arrival to Professor Walther. He was shown up to the study, where the professor with a long German pipe in his mouth was seated in the midst of a great pile of papers and books. He was an old man, almost skinny, with a little fringe of hair around his neck and ears which seemed to join a band of gray beard under his chin. His eyes were deep-set and clear, and his large curved nose almost touched his chin.

He rose at once. "Well, my dear young friend, I suppose you are one of the new students."

Halvor began to explain who he was, but he found to his chagrin that he could not speak German as glibly as he had expected. He managed to give his name, and presented his credentials from Luther College.

"Then you are one of our dear Norwegian students? You are heartily welcome! Our Norwegian brethren have always brought us joy. Any one of the older students will tell you what books to buy and other such information." And with a cordial handshake and a "God keep you, my young friend," he dismissed Halvor and returned to his work.

As soon as classes began, the Norwegian students realized how hard it would be to keep up with the Germans. They had to become fluent in German, and that was not easy. For four or five hours a day they had to listen to lectures and take notes for dear life. In the evening, when they tried to go over their notes in preparation for the next day's quiz, they usually found them as obscure as if they had been written in Assyrian cuneiform.

The Germans had the great advantage, not only of knowing the language, but also—at least many of them—of knowing shorthand. On the whole, they were able fellows, a little younger than their Norwegian classmates. They had come from the *gymnasium* at Fort Wayne in their natural wild state; but gradually, as they pursued their theological studies, they learned civilized manners. When they had finished their seminary course, they were ready and willing to accept a call to the most impoverished parish, to work like slaves, and to suffer, if need be, for "the pure doctrine."[4]

The teachers at the seminary were old-fashioned and scholarly. Professor Schaller was always so friendly that one could not help loving him. Professor Guenther was dry and taciturn, but was presumed to possess an incredible store of learning. The students said of him that, like General Von Moltke, he was able to keep silence in a score of languages. Then there was old Pastor Brohm, who would walk back and forth in the Aula with his hands behind his back, teaching Hebrew; although blind, he was said to know the Hebrew Bible by heart.

And finally there was Professer Walther himself. Because of his strong personality he seemed to Halvor and the other students the very incarnation of simple childlike faith and profound scholarship. His lectures were given

---

[4] The college at Fort Wayne, Indiana, was modeled on the German *gymnasium*. The Missouri Synod, during its early years under the leadership of Professor Walther, stressed "the pure doctrine" *(die reine Lehre)* to the point where, among Norwegian-American Lutherans, at least, the phrase became something of a byword.

in a hall in the library near his home. He always appeared for his classes on the stroke of the clock, and he demanded the same punctuality from his students. As a teacher he was strict; he would not tolerate bluffing, nor bad Latin. The favorite class of the week, and the one by which the students reckoned the days, was the so-called Luther Hour every Friday evening from seven to eight, when Professor Walther lectured in the Aula on a subject proposed by the students themselves, while his listeners sat pulling on their pipes and taking down in their notebooks some unusually striking expression.

It might be thought that the Norwegian students, so few in number, would have felt like strangers among so many Germans, but this was by no means true. They had a most cordial comradeship. If the teachers showed any partiality, it was in giving the Norwegians, whom they regarded somewhat as guests, a little more attention and freedom than the Germans. The reputation of the Norwegian students at St. Louis was excellent. It was assumed that they were all exemplary young men and would stoop to nothing wrong. They were welcomed into the best families of the German congregations of the city and they almost always got the best of the *Waschtanten*.

This last expression needs an explanation. Every nonresident student was assigned to a family; during his student days he was to all intents and purposes considered a member of it. In the home of this family he could spend Sundays and other holidays. There, too, his clothes were washed and mended. For this reason the mother of the house was called his *Waschtante* or "wash aunt." There were always enough kindly disposed families willing to take in students and care for them in this way.

Halvor was assigned to a well-to-do elderly widow, who at once seemed to regard him as a near and dear relative. Such a hospitable arrangement was much appreciated, for board at the seminary was certainly nothing to brag about. Most of the students could not afford to pay for lordly fare; besides, the German school authorities seemed to think a young man would take hold of his theological studies with greater zeal if he were constantly hungry.

Halvor could not stand it. He longingly recalled the fleshpots at home, and he and other inmates of Asgaard bought a frying pan. When the fare had been altogether too Spartan for a few days, they would "nickel up," or pool their resources, and buy sausage and beer and other good things, and have a simple little feast.

Living on such meager fare made the Christmas and Easter holidays, which the Norwegian students spent with some hospitable German farmers near Collinsville, Illinois, all the more festive. They went there in a body and were always made welcome. Up to this time these Germans had never seen Norwegians; at first they were surprised to find the latter to be ordinary white people and not a species of Eskimo, as they had earlier imagined.

The Germans at Collinsville were very capable and enterprising. They were not a large group, but they had their own church, schoolhouse, parsonage, and teacherage, their own minister, and two regularly hired teachers. Like all genuine German Lutherans, they were extremely genial and seemed to be on a surprisingly familiar footing with the Lord. They always spoke of "der liebe Gott" as of a respected member of the family, one whom they ought to thank, whose will they always wanted to follow.

Professor Walther was the pastor of a large congregation in St. Louis, divided into four districts, each with its own church and an assistant pastor. It was only occasionally therefore, that Walther himself preached in these churches. When it was known that he was to preach, the Norwegian students made a point of attending and, by following him from church to church, often heard the same sermon more than once. For he always wrote out his sermons and committed them to memory. Occasionally he acted as organist in the church nearest the seminary; then the students who had missed being present were always very put out at not having known that he was to play.

Now and then the Norwegian students went to one of the German churches to hear the old giant, Pastor Buenger, thunder against the Papacy and its teachings. But mostly they attended the services of a little Danish congregation which met every Sunday in the schoolhouse of a German congregation. They themselves took turns preaching, for the congregation had no pastor.

Here, toward the close of his first year, Halvor Helgeson was to preach his first sermon. For three months he had worked on it; yet, when the hour came, he felt that it fell far short of what a sermon ought to be. He needed more time. Moreover, he was not sure whether, all things considered, he was called to preach. He had such serious misgivings! After a great deal of encouragement from one of the older students, he took heart and said he would try. Moreover, he had just been reading George Eliot's *Romola* and had been thinking not a little about Savonarola, the great forerunner of the Reformation. This courageous Christian hero admitted that he "often had to preach on the faith he had yesterday in hope that it would come back to him tomorrow."

Halvor, then, preached his sermon in fear and trembling. He had learned it so well that he did not falter. When it was over, he slipped quietly out of the schoolhouse and over to his *Waschtante*. He did not want to face his companions—for they remembered all the mad pranks he had played in Decorah. But when he met them again, they comforted him by saying his sermon was really pretty good. Yet, one of them thought it had been constructed almost too much according to formula and was a little too obvious. It had reminded him, he said, of the following well-known outline:

Today we shall consider the subject of "The Two Disciples on the Way to Emmaus."

We shall see:

Firstly, how many there were.

And secondly, whither they were going.

CHAPTER NINETEEN

The pledging of Nora

Halvor had struggled through his first year; he was enjoying the prospect of a summer vacation in the North with his own people. The Germans were all right; but, just the same, they were strangers. His father sent him money with permission to go home by way of Decorah so that he might attend the Synod meeting, to be held there that year.

The school term in St. Louis extended to the last of June; but the faculty had somehow acquired the notion that the Norwegians, coming as they did from so far north, could not stand the hot summer weather of St. Louis, and gave them permission to leave for home several weeks early.

Halvor and the other Norwegian students who were not graduating left early in June, taking a steamboat up the Mississippi to McGregor, Iowa. This was slow travel, to be sure; but that was all the better. They were in no hurry.

What an enjoyable trip they had! Nothing to worry about. Wherever the boat stopped long enough, they took a walk into town to see the sights. They enjoyed watching the roustabouts working and sweating. And they made certain they were the first at table when the dinner bell rang. The food and their appetites were equally excellent. At night it was pleasant to lie on deck and smoke, gazing at the many dark shadowy forms between which the boat plowed its way.

Among the passengers was a Roman Catholic priest. Two of the students thought it their duty as orthodox Lutheran theologians to use what they had learned in St. Louis and convince him of the errors of the Papacy. For a whole day they strove to convert him, but to no avail. He remained obdurate; he would not even admit what to Halvor Helgeson was especially important: namely, that the clergy should be allowed to marry.

Once the steamboat grounded on a sand bar and there was a long-drawn-out struggle to get it afloat again. Halvor did not mind in the least. He had paid for transportation, with board and lodging, to McGregor, even if it took a month to get there. In spite of everything, however, in five days the boat lay to at the dock in McGregor. That same afternoon Halvor stepped off the train in Decorah.

How good it was to see Decorah and Luther College again after a whole year's absence! And to revisit all the old haunts and sit at the table with the boys in the dining hall! Why, they even had the very same waitresses! And then to go swimming again, in the very same place where seven years ago he had learned to swim. Everything was a sheer delight. Halvor felt as if he were still just a boy. In the evening he went to the smoking room in the "Chicken Coop," arriving just in time to hear a lively debate. It seems that a bug had been found in the tobacco box. Jensen proposed that the bug be admitted to the society as an advisory member, but someone else made a substitute motion that it should merely be invited to take a seat. This fine distinction was what caused the heated debate.

Because of the Synod meeting, classes at Luther College closed a few days before the regular time. Halvor had the pleasure of being present at the commencement exercises, as well as at an evening party given in honor of Professor Landmark, who was going back to Norway to live.

The Synod meeting, the last to be held before the church body was divided into three districts, drew a large crowd to Decorah. Halvor Helgeson and the other students from St. Louis were honored, as was the custom, by being accepted as advisory members, an action which caused a couple of college boys to grin at Halvor from across the hall, to remind him of the debate the night before in Niffelheim.

Besides the many capable men who were delegates to the Synod meeting, there were a few queer ducks who helped make the occasion interesting to anyone who, like our good friend Helgeson, had a sense of humor. One man, for instance, about to offer his contribution to a doctrinal discussion, prefaced his remarks thus, "I am only a layman and have no book learning, but I have uncommonly good understanding and great discretion."

Such a man it might pay to get acquainted with. So Halvor sought him out in the evening after the meeting and engaged him in conversation. The man was now more at ease and talked quite freely. "Norway," he said, "is what I would call practically a heathen country. They learn nothing but the catechism and the question book.[1] I'm a bright fellow, you see; but I never got no book learning."

"But in this country things are no doubt better in that respect," ventured Halvor.

"Oh, yes, but I was too old to learn anything here."

"You've no doubt attended other Synod meetings haven't you?"

"Only one. At that meeting I managed to put through a motion they had been fussing over for three years. I said: 'Preus,' said I, 'I give all the Norwegian pastors in America,' said I, 'power and authority to start good Norwegian parochial schools,' said I. And Ottesen—you know Ottesen, of course, from Kaskeland—he said, 'I second the motion.' And the motion carried."

After the meeting Halvor drove home with Pastor Dahlby and visited for a couple of weeks in that dear parsonage. And since he now was once again so near, it was only reasonable for him to call at Anderson's once in a while—especially of an evening. During the day Nora was teaching school in the neighborhood—not that that really mattered. Mr.

---

[1] The catechism and the question book are actually the same, "question book" being a Norwegian colloquial name for the catechism.

Halvor said: "Nora, there's something I want to tell you

Anderson was a very intelligent man and no doubt it was the pleasure of visiting with him that attracted Halvor. But it so happened that it was not much farther to Anderson's if he took the road past the schoolhouse. It was mere coincidence, of course, that he walked past the schoolhouse every afternoon just when Nora was leaving for home. Naturally, he accompanied her. Then they would talk a great deal about all sorts of trifling things. Halvor found that she grew more bewitchingly charming every day.

The only fly in the ointment was her little sister, who was attending school and insisted on walking home with them. It was exasperating! It was impossible to have a real talk with Nora while that youngster tagged along. But one afternoon Nora sent the child home early, and quite by chance Halvor happened by that very day—at just the right time. Nora, the little witch, looked as if she suspected him of having something on his mind. It proved to be so. When they reached a valley and had sat down on the trunk of a tree to rest for a moment, Halvor said:

"Nora, there's something I want to tell you. If it weren't for the fact that students at the seminary in St. Louis are strictly forbidden to become engaged, I'd ask you a question. But now I'll have to put it off for two whole years. I want you to know, however, that I'll ask it then. And what do you think you'll answer then?"

Nora looked down and whispered, "I think I'll answer yes."

"I'm certainly glad to hear that. Be sure no one comes and takes you away from me in the meantime."

And that was all. It was as matter-of-fact as that.

When Halvor got back to the parsonage, Pastor Dahlby said, "Well, have you been over to Anderson's again? You look very happy. Is it in order, perhaps, to congratulate you?"

"No," stammered Halvor. "It's against the rules at St. Louis for a student to have any other sweetheart than theology."

"Yes, but something happened over there," said the minister. "What is it?"

"Oh, nothing, except that I asked Nora what she would say two years from now, when I expect to ask her if she will move in with me!"

"And what did she reply?"

"She thought she would answer yes."

"Well, that's a great way to obey the rules of the seminary! But there's no need to worry. In such matters one does not follow rules."

Now Halvor went home to spend the rest of the summer with his parents before returning to St. Louis.

"It certainly took you an awfully long time to get here from Decorah," said Soren.

"I visited Pastor Dahlby's," said Halvor. "And there's something else I think I should tell you. Near the parsonage there is a family named Anderson. And I've spent quite a little time there, especially since they have a daughter whom I like. Her name is Nora."

"But, my dear boy, wouldn't it be best to wait with such things until you are dry behind the ears? Let me see —how old are you?"

"Oh, you know that I'm just old enough to vote for Tilden for president this fall."

Soren gave such a start that he forgot about Nora completely. All he could think of—and it really pained him to do so—was that Halvor was going to vote for Tilden, that Democrat, for president. "What are you saying, boy? You're going to vote for Tilden? So that's what you learn in St. Louis. If I thought you were serious, I'd———."

"No, no, I'm not serious, Father. I'll vote for Hayes, of course. But what I was trying to say is that I'm now twenty-one."

"Well, I guess you really are. But how you frightened me with that talk about Tilden!"

Soren was so relieved that Halvor had not turned Democrat that he forgot to say anything more about Nora.

Since Halvor was now a theological student, he was invited to preach in his home church. For years everyone had been waiting to hear "that there boy of Soren Helgeson's." So, one Sunday morning, he preached the only sermon he had ready. When he mounted the pulpit and caught sight of his father and mother sitting in the front row with misty eyes, his knees began to shake. Right beside them sat Jens and Helga Knudson, happy in the certainty that now at last they would hear a preacher who was the equal of Pastor Harbitz.

Halvor did himself proud, and people thought it marvelous how fluently he spoke and how extraordinarily well he knew his Bible. They did not know he had worked at that sermon for three months and could have preached it in his sleep.

The next day, when Halvor visited his godparents, he was received with greater respect than ever before. "But I certainly don't think you should call him Halvor any longer now," said Helga to Jens. "Say, what is it we should call you, Halvor? We saw your name in print in *The Church Times*, and it said 'Stud. Helgeson.' What kind of titulation is that to give a person, I should like to know?"

Halvor explained that it meant only "student."

"Well, didn't I tell you, Jens, that that was what it must mean and it was nothing to get mad about? But I guess we'll have to call you Halvor, anyway, seeing we've always known you. For it was me, you know, that brought you into the world."

"Yes, of course. Just call me Halvor. That's good enough for me."

"It seems queer to think how learned you've become," said Jens. "But then you've had a learned father, too. If I just had his learning and could read and write and reckon like he can, I wouldn't go slaving around here on a farm."

"What would you do?"

"Oh, I'd go down to Chicago and get a job in the stock-yards."

Halvor spent this summer, too, working on the farm. Again he worked so hard that his father thought it was too much of a good thing, that it was not necessary to go at it quite so earnestly.

In due time he went back to St. Louis. The second year passed much as the first, except that his studies grew more and more interesting, and the end of the year seemed to come before he was prepared for it. He was home again for the summer vacation, preached a couple of sermons he had written in St. Louis, and then one day in the middle of August, he said to his father: "Well, it's no doubt a relief to know that this is the last year you'll have to give me money. But, if you think you can afford it, I'd like to leave now and go by Decorah and visit Pastor Dahlby."

"Oh, I guess that's all right, if you want it that way. You're enough of a man now to do as you like. But

I think you might just as well come out with the truth and admit it is not Pastor Dahlby but someone else you're so eager to see."

So Halvor had a chance to reassure himself that all was well in the Halling settlement and yet reach St. Louis in time for the opening of school.

There was so much to learn during the last year that he did not see how he could cover it all, but he did his best. Professor Walther's lectures to the third-year students every Thursday evening on the subject "Science Intoxicated, or Modern Science, neither Scientific nor Divine" were so eloquent that Halvor wished he could listen to them for another year. The same was true of his lectures on pastoral theology. They gave students a new outlook upon the work that was ahead and made grown men out of those who until then had been boys. For once Halvor had no fear of the final examination. He had learned his Baier's *Dogmatics* by heart and had at his fingertips the statement defining "the pure doctrine." The examination demonstrated that he was able to translate a chapter of the Old Testament from Hebrew to Latin, knew the mode of procedure in matters of church discipline, could outline the introduction of the Reformation to the Scandinavian countries, could give the explanation of the eighth commandment in Luther's *Large Catechism*, and knew the heretical views of Socinus and Cochlaeus concerning the millennium.

He therefore received a diploma stating he had studied theology with great diligence, had lived an exemplary life, and had demonstrated that he was well prepared. All the above was attested to in behalf of the faculty by C. F. W. Walther, S.S. *Theologiae doctor et professor.*

Through the Church Council of the Norwegian Synod Halvor had already received a letter of call from several small congregations in Morris County, Minnesota, and he decided to accept. He could hardly be suspected of taking the call for mercenary reasons, for in the letter the congregation stated expressly that the members "could promise no fixed salary but would, according to their means, contribute to the pastor's frugal support."

After saying goodbye to his teachers, *Waschtante,* and other friends in St. Louis, Halvor again visited Decorah. There he at once became aware that he was no longer a schoolboy but a theological candidate, for Professor Larsen now used the polite pronoun "De" in addressing him instead of the familiar form "du." Next he visited Pastor Dahlby's and then Anderson's. He could wait no longer. With no beating around the bush he told Nora's parents his errand. They replied that she herself would have to decide. Then he looked for Nora.

He found her in the garden, a bouquet of sweet peas in her hand. He had only one thing on his mind.

"I suppose you'll move to Morris County with me as soon as I've been there and found a house?"

"What do you mean?"

"Well, I suppose you intend to———"

"How do you know what my intentions are?"

"You haven't forgotten what you promised, have you?"

"No, but I might have changed my mind."

"Well, have you changed it, then?"

"No, silly, I certainly haven't."

"Oh, you tease. You little witch." And he gathered her into his arms and held her close.

A month later Helga Knudson, at home in Springville, read the following from *The Church Times* to Jens, inserting her own comments on it:

On the sixth Sunday after Trinity, the twenty-eighth of July, in Red Wing, Minnesota, Candidate Halvor Helgeson was ordained to the holy ministry by the Reverend B. J. Muus, president of the Minnesota District. The ordination sermon was preached by the Reverend Mr. Bøckman, who read the following *vita* or biography, written by the candidate:

Halvor Helgeson—"now, listen, Jens,"—was born July 15, 1855, in Springville, Wisconsin—"Yes, I remember it as if it were yesterday"—to Soren Helgeson and wife Signe, nee Holte—"Why, that isn't true, Jens, Signe was born in Tuddal. I've heard her tell it myself."—In his home he received a good bringing up and was confirmed at the age of fourteen by Pastor Evensen. Immediately after confirmation, in the fall of 1869, he entered Luther College, Decorah, Iowa, at which institution he completed the prescribed courses. Thereupon he attended the theoretical-theological seminary at St. Louis, where he studied for three years. At the examinations held this summer he was found to be well prepared for the office of the holy ministry. He has now accepted a call from Trinity and Six Mile Creek Congregations in Morris County, Minnesota.

As Helga wiped her eyes, she added: "Isn't it strange to be sitting here reading about him? And Anne says he's now engaged, and that she's rich, too. And here I've known him since the day he was born!"

"Yes, folks like him," said Jens, "generally get the one they want. Now, take Pastor Harbitz. Why, he married the daughter of a captain! His name was—bless me, if I haven't forgotten his name!"

CHAPTER TWENTY

Pastor Helgeson

Young Pastor Helgeson had now served half a year in his congregations. His parishioners received him with cordiality, but had very little more to offer him. It was hard work. He traveled far and wide, organizing congregations among the settlers. Now there were so many that he could barely get around to them once a month. Perhaps it was just as well that he still had no home of his own. He had had to write to his father for money to buy a horse and buggy. The money came but Halvor was taken in on a horse deal; now he rattled over the wide prairies with a miserable nag that was barely able to put one foot in front of the other. He sought lodging in the cabins of the settlers wherever he chanced to be. The cabins consisted usually of only one room; and when the minister came, he would sleep with the man of the house in the bed, while the wife and children slept in the trundle bed on the floor.

But Helgeson made the best of things and was as undaunted as ever. He was welcome everywhere. People no doubt thought he was rather young and almost too cheerful to be a preacher, but none the less they found his visits refreshing. The congregations at this time were plagued by sundry fly-by-night preachers who went from house to house, frightening people so sorely with their lurid talk of hell-fire that Halvor had to make the rounds after them, airing out the houses after their visits, and by word and example impressing upon his people that God is good and that one of a Christian's first duties is to be happy.

There was another species of tramp who traveled about making capital of the credulity of the settlers. One day, as Pastor Helgeson was driving past a schoolhouse in which he was to preach, he noticed a placard nailed to the door. It read thus:

A lectjer will be held here next Sunday afternoon at 4 o'clock by Halvor Pederson. He will take as his subject Is it true that there is a life after this.

The adres will be a trial of both sides of the question only illuminated by Nature without drawing the slightest recourse to the Bible. Everyone who wants to hear a philosophic subject scientifically treated is most heartily welkum. Admission 10¢.

With such learned lecturers, Helgeson had many a long and wearisome battle.

230

Pastor and Mrs. Helgeson

People thought it marvelous that he managed to get around in all sorts of weather. When the winter storms made roads so impassable that hardly anyone dared leave home, he would shovel his way through the snowdrifts.

He had hoped that his Christmas offering would be big enough to enable him to buy a little house and go and get Nora. But at Christmastime the weather was so bad that he was almost the only one to break the way to the schoolhouses where he was to preach. This was a great disappointment.

Not until months later could he at last write Nora that he had a parsonage. The house, he told her, was sixteen feet short and twelve feet narrow and there were only two small rooms. But if she would come, her arrival would change it into a veritable palace. And Helgeson, scraping together a little money, went down to the Halling settlement and came back a few days later richer than he had ever been before.

The people of his congregation could not help liking Nora. It was impossible not to do so. As she found it tiresome to stay home alone, she nearly always went with Halvor on his drives. Now and then, when they had an opportunity to be home together for a few days, it was a festival for them both. The house was so neat and clean and the mistress of it so fascinatingly sweet and beautiful that Halvor would forget he was now a dignified clergyman, put his arms around her waist, and dance her about the room. "Nora, my dear, I'm as happy as twenty kings!"

One year passed and another. Things went smoothly until the bitter election or predestination controversy broke out in the Norwegian Synod.

"What is the fuss all about?" Nora asked her husband. "I don't understand it."

"Well, it's not easy to explain," said Halvor. "It's a difficult theological question."

"I know, but just what is it?"

"It's a question of how man is elected to salvation. Are those elected picked out by God—that would be predestination—or does a man have a chance to say yes or no to God's invitation?"

"But why call them Missourians or Anti-Missourians?"

"Oh, those who hold the view of the Missouri Synod are called Missourians; the others, Anti-Missourians."

"Which ones believe in predestination, then?" asked Nora.

232

"That's the strange part of it," said Halvor. "Neither side will admit that. But they can't agree on how man is elected to salvation. Frankly, I think it's a theological mystery."

"Well, I can't make head or tail of it. I should think love of God would be enough."

"Nora, your good heart is worth more than a dozen theologians."

Halvor tried to keep his congregations free from strife. He did not like the finespun, hairsplitting theological arguments. Moreover, there were other matters on his mind. One would hardly recognize the house, for an addition had been made to the parsonage and there were now four rooms. One of them actually had a carpet. And over by the stove there was a cradle.

One fall day Nora and her maid were busy in the kitchen. Every now and then Nora went to the window and looked down the road expectantly. Halvor's father, who had been unable to attend the wedding and so had not yet seen his daughter-in-law, was coming to visit them for the first time. Halvor had gone to meet him.

There they came. Nora ran out to greet them. She could see at a glance that the tall strong man with the blond beard was Halvor's father. "Halvor will look just like him when he grows old," she thought. Going straight to Soren, she gave him a kiss.

He held her at arm's length. "Well, Halvor," he laughed, while Nora blushed prettily, "love was certainly not blind in your case." But there was another man in the buggy, a lame little fellow who now climbed down.

"Who do you think this is, Nora?" said Halvor. "It's our old neighbor Jens Knudson."

Nora held out her hand. "How nice of you to come with Father! You are more than welcome. Please come in now, all of you."

They entered the house and quietly admired little Soren, sleeping peacefully in his cradle. Then they sat down and began to visit, Halvor with his father and Nora with old Jens.

"Halvor has spoken of you so often that I feel as if I have always known you," she said. "It was so kind of you to come. You have made Halvor and me very happy."

Jens was all but overcome by her graciousness. Compelled to express his feelings somehow, without a word he took a bill from his pocketbook, stepped over to the cradle, and laid it gravely beside little Soren.

"Oh, that is much too generous of you!" said Nora, her heart warming to the little old man who all these years had been so loyal to her husband. Jens, looking rather embarrassed, smiled shyly.

"Now we must have something to eat," Nora added. "I imagine you are all starved. And I must look after this little rascal." With that she took little Soren out to the other room.

While Nora and the maid were busy with their preparations, Halvor turned to his father. "Now tell us all about the folks in Springville. How is everything back home?"

"Oh, there isn't much to tell. Mother is well, and Jenny, as you know, is engaged to our new minister. There's trouble in the congregation again, however. People are disputing about Calvinism and synergism or some other sort of *ism*, and it looks as if the congregation will split wide open again."

"That's bad, isn't it?" Halvor remarked. "Jens, which side are you on?"

"Well, I s'pose I'll have to be on the same side as Helga, for she knows all about such things. And she says she wants to be on the same side as Preus. I guess they call it Missouri or Mississippi or something like that."

"Are you having the same trouble here, Halvor?" asked Soren.

"No, not too much; it's still quite peaceful here. There's more talk about the price of wheat than about election and predestination."

"Well, I'm glad you're not having the trouble we're having," said his father. "But Halvor, tell me, what is really your opinion about this election or predestination business, whatever you call it?"

"Oh, to tell you the truth, I haven't been lying awake nights thinking about it. It's a very difficult and involved affair, perhaps a mystery best left alone by mortals. But in my own simple way I am inclined to believe what a certain wise man has said, namely, that one can't expect to be elected unless he agrees to be a candidate."

Soren laughed quietly. "Well, that's about what I think, too. But I guess we can't settle the matter."

Just then Nora brought in a little blondhead and turned him over to Halvor. "Here he is, wide-awake at last. Take care of him a few minutes, will you? Dinner is almost ready."

"So this is the new generation! Well, he's a fine bouncing boy, Halvor. Let me get a good look at him. What do you think, Jens? Will he look like his father?"

"Oh, I'm not much good at such things. Helga, though, she could tell. She could tell right away. And she's always right. It's too bad she wasn't here to help out."

"Yes, Helga would have had an answer, all right," said Soren. "But this little fellow will get along, whether he looks like Halvor or not. Have you decided what he's going to be when he grows up?"

"Perhaps it's a little too early for that," replied Halvor.

"Oh, yes, there's plenty of time. But you're going to see to it that he gets an education."

"Yes, yes, no doubt about that."

"Perhaps you'll be sending him to that school in Decorah?"

"You mean do what you did with me? Well, that could be—that could be."

"Dinner's ready," called Nora, and they all went in together.

Copies of *HALVOR* may be ordered from the Luther College Book Shop, Decorah, Iowa.